GCSE OCR Gateway
Physics
Higher Workbook

This book is for anyone doing **GCSE OCR Gateway Physics** at higher level.

It's full of **tricky questions**... each one designed to make you **sweat**
— because that's the only way you'll get any **better**.

There are questions to see **what facts** you know. There are questions
to see how well you can **apply those facts**. And there are questions
to see what you know about **how science works**.

It's also got some daft bits in to try and make the whole
experience at least vaguely entertaining for you.

What CGP is all about

Our sole aim here at CGP is to produce the highest
quality books — carefully written, immaculately presented
and dangerously close to being funny.

Then we work our socks off to get them
out to you — at the cheapest possible prices.

Contents

MODULE P4 — RADIATION FOR LIFE

MODULE P5 — SPACE FOR REFLECTION

MODULE P6 — ELECTRICITY FOR GADGETS

Published by Coordination Group Publications Ltd.

Editors:
Tom Cain, Gemma Hallam, Sarah Hilton, Sharon Keeley, Ami Snelling, Sarah Williams.

Contributors:
Tony Alldridge, Peter Cecil, Steve Coggins, Vikki Cunningham, Mark A Edwards, Andrew Furze, Giles Greenway, Frederick Langridge, Barbara Mascetti, John Myers, Pat Szczesniak, Paul Warren, Andy Williams, Jim Wilson.

From original material by Paddy Gannon

With thanks to Ian Francis, Andy Park, Steve Parkinson and Glenn Rogers for the proofreading.

ISBN: 978 1 84146 471 8

Groovy website: www.cgpbooks.co.uk

Printed by Elanders Hindson Ltd, Newcastle upon Tyne.
Jolly bits of clipart from CorelDRAW®

Moving and Storing Heat

Q1 Complete these sentences by circling the correct word from each pair.

Heat is a measure of hotness / energy.

Temperature is a measure of hotness / energy.

Heat travels from a hot / cold place to a hot / cold place.

Water is a good material for storing heat because it has a high / low specific heat capacity.

When a substance is heated its particles vibrate more / less quickly.

Q2 **Temperature** can be measured on various **scales**.

a) Give an example of a scale used to measure temperature. ....

b) Everyday **temperature** scales go **lower than zero**. Explain why
it isn't possible to have a measurement of **heat** that is below zero.

....

....

Q3 a) What is **specific heat capacity**?

....

b) Agatha has 1 kg samples of two substances — A and B. Substance **A** has a   Substance A
higher specific heat capacity than substance B. Both samples cool down
by 10 °C. Which will release more heat — A or B? Circle the correct answer.   Substance B

Q4 Mildred thinks she could make her hot water bottle more efficient by filling it with **mercury**, which
has a specific heat capacity of **139 J/kg /°C** . The specific heat capacity of water is **4200 J/kg /°C**.

Work out the **difference** in energy released by two litres of mercury cooling
from 70 °C to 20 °C and two litres of water cooling from 70 °C to 20 °C .   *Don't try this at home*
(2 l of mercury has a mass of 27.2 kg. 2 l of water has a mass of 2 kg.)   *— mercury's toxic at*
any temperature.

....

....

....

....

Q5 A piece of copper is heated to **90 °C** and then lowered into a beaker of water which is at **20 °C**.
The copper transfers **3040 J** of energy to the water before it is removed. The temperature of the
copper after it is removed is **50 °C**. The specific heat capacity of copper is **380 J/kg/°C**.

Calculate the **mass** of the copper. ....

....

<u>Melting and Boiling</u>

Q1 The graph shows the temperature change as a substance is heated up.
The letters A to E represent each **state** of the substance and each **change of state**.

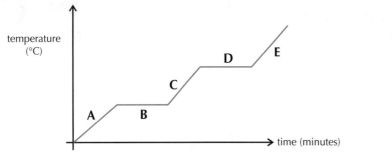

Boiling	A
Gas	B
Liquid	C
Melting	D
Solid	E

Join each state or change of state to the correct letter.

Q2 A beaker of pure water is heated. When it reaches 100 °C it **stays** at 100 °C, even though it is **still being heated**. Which of sentences A-D is the correct explanation for why this happens? Circle the correct letter.

A Energy is being lost to the surroundings as quickly as it is being supplied to the beaker.

B The pan is absorbing the extra energy.

C The energy supplied is being used to break intermolecular bonds and change the water to steam.

D A more powerful heater should have been used.

Q3 The graph shows what happens to the temperature of a beaker of **molten wax** as it cools to room temperature.

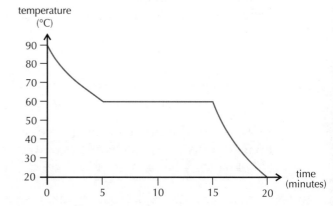

a) At what temperature does the wax become **solid** again?

....

b) Explain why the temperature of the wax **remains constant** during solidification.

....

....

c) From the start of solidification, **how long** did it take before all the liquid wax became solid?

....

Top Tips: The next page has some nice **sums** all about melting and boiling. Melting and boiling calculations always involve **specific latent heat** — definitely not to be confused with **specific heat capacity**. Remember, while a substance is changing state, its temperature doesn't change. So don't try to use a formula with 'temperature change' in it for melting or boiling sums — it won't work.

Melting and Boiling

Q4   A kettle supplies energy at a rate of **2500 J per second**. It contains 1.5 litres of water which is at 100 °C. **How long** would the kettle need to boil for in order to **evaporate** all this water? (The specific latent heat of water for boiling is 2.26 MJ/kg. 1 litre of water has a mass of 1 kg.)

....

....

....

Q5   Answer the following questions using the information in the table.

Substance	Melting Point (°C)	Specific latent heat of melting (kJ/kg)
Water (ice)	0	334
Aluminium	658	396
Copper	1083	205
Lead	327	23
Zinc	419	110

a)   A heater supplies **500 kJ** of thermal energy over **10 minutes**.

    i) Use the table to calculate the **mass of ice** at 0 °C that it could melt in 10 minutes.

    ....

    ....

    ii) Use the table to calculate the **mass of zinc** at 419 °C that it could melt in 10 minutes.

    ....

    ....

b)   Dave puts **ice** in his lemonade to cool it down. The ice melts. Calculate the energy transferred to **30 g** of ice cubes by **300 g** of lemonade as the ice melts.

....

c)   A heater supplies energy to **2 kg of lead** at 20 °C. The energy supplied is used to increase its temperature. The temperature of the lead keeps increasing and then stays at the **same temperature**. While the lead stays at the same temperature, what is the energy supplied **used** for?

....

Conduction and Convection in the Home

Q1   Tick to show whether the sentences are true or false.

True False

a)   Conduction involves **energy** passing between **vibrating particles**.   ☐ ☐

b)   Some **metals** are very **poor** conductors.   ☐ ☐

c)   **Solids** are usually better **conductors** of heat than liquids and gases.   ☐ ☐

d)   **Plastic** is a **poor** conductor because it contains **free electrons**.   ☐ ☐

Q2   George picks up a piece of wood and a metal spoon. Both are at the same temperature: 20 °C.

Explain why the metal spoon feels **colder** to the touch than the piece of wood.

....

....

Q3   Great Aunt Marjorie knits blankets for babies. She says that a blanket **with holes** in keeps a baby **warmer** than a blanket without holes in. Why is this?

....

....

Q4   Match each observation with an explanation.

The very bottom of a hot water tank stays cold...

because water isn't a good heat conductor.

Warm air rises...

because heat flows from warm places to cooler ones.

A small heater can send heat all over a room...

because it is not so dense.

Q5   Sam uses the apparatus shown to investigate **heat transfer** in water.

He heats the middle of the tube with a Bunsen flame.
The ice at the top of the tube melts quickly,
but the ice at the bottom does not melt.

Ice floating at the top

Glass tube full of cold water

Ice weighted so it stays at the bottom

What does this experiment show about conduction and convection in water? Explain your answer.

....

....

....

Heat Radiation

Q1 Tick the sentences below to show whether they are **true** or **false**.

True False

a) The amount of heat radiation absorbed by a surface depends only on its colour. ☐ ☐

b) The hotter a surface is, the more heat it radiates. ☐ ☐

c) Good absorbers of heat are also good emitters of heat. ☐ ☐

d) Heat is radiated as ultraviolet waves. ☐ ☐

e) All objects are constantly absorbing and emitting heat radiation. ☐ ☐

f) Heat radiation can travel through a vacuum. ☐ ☐

Q2 Mr Jones and Ms Smith each put a **solar hot water panel** on the roof of their houses.

Write down two reasons why Ms Smith gets more hot water than Mr Jones.

1. ....

....

2. ....

Ms Smith's house

Mr Jones' house

Q3 Complete the following by circling the correct word from each pair.

a) **Dark**, **matt** surfaces are **good** / **poor** absorbers and **good** / **poor** emitters of heat radiation.

b) The best surfaces for **radiating** heat are **good** / **poor** absorbers and **good** / **poor** emitters.

c) The best materials for making **survival blankets** are **good** / **poor** absorbers and **good** / **poor** emitters.

d) The best surfaces for **solar hot water panels** are **good** / **poor** absorbers and **good** / **poor** emitters.

Q4 When a piece of bread is heated in a **toaster** the outside of the bread **darkens** as it toasts.

You're far too young to be smoking.

a) How is **energy transferred** from the element in the toaster to the bread? ....

b) **Brown bread** toasts a little bit **more quickly** than white bread. Explain why this is.

....

c) The **middle** of the bread will also warm up, but much more **slowly** than the outside. Explain why.

....

....

d) Paul lines his grill pan with **shiny foil**. How does this help him **grill sausages** more effectively?

....

....

Heat Radiation

Q5 Tim did an investigation using a **Leslie's cube**.
Each surface on the cube had a different combination of **colour** and **texture**.

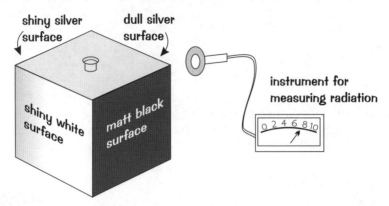

Tim measured the heat radiation coming from each surface. His results are shown below.

Surface	Reading	Colour and Texture
A	10	
B	4	dull silver
C	4	
D	2	

a) Complete the table to show which was:

i) the **matt black** surface.

ii) the **shiny silver** surface.

iii) the **shiny white** surface.

b) Tim's friend Julie copied his results for the experiment.
She then wrote a conclusion —

"**Dull silver and shiny white surfaces always emit the same amount of radiation.**"

Explain what is wrong with Julie's conclusion.

....

....

c) Which of the surfaces A to D would be best to use for the outside of a refrigerator?
Explain your answer.

....

....

Saving Energy

Q1 A **thermogram** can show where heat energy is escaping from a house.

Study the thermogram of three terraced houses **X**, **Y** and **Z** below.
For each description below, write the correct letter **X**, **Y** or **Z** in the box.

least heat lost ⟶ most heat lost

a) This house has good loft and window insulation but poor wall insulation.

b) This house has double glazing and cavity wall insulation, but poor loft insulation.

c) This house has good thick loft insulation and cavity wall insulation but it has poorly insulated windows with no double glazing.

Q2 Draw arrows to match up the **words** with their **meanings**.

Cost

Cost-effectiveness

Payback time

Effectiveness

How much energy you save.

How much you have to pay.

How long it takes to save as much as you spent initially.

How worthwhile it is to spend the money.

Q3 Explain how the following types of insulation work.

a) Cavity wall insulation ....

....

b) Loft insulation ....

....

c) Hot water tank jacket ....

....

Module P1 — Energy for the Home

Saving Energy

Q4 Heat is lost from a house through its **roof**, **walls**, **doors** and **windows**.

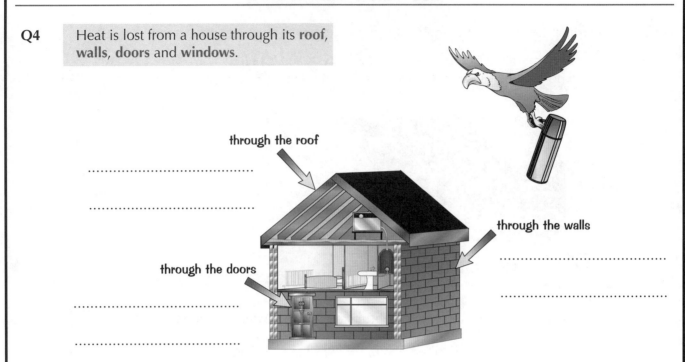

through the roof

....

....

through the walls

....

....

through the doors

....

....

a) In the spaces on the diagram, write down at least one measure that could be taken to reduce heat losses through each part of the house.

b) Miss Golightly has just bought a new house which has very large windows. Suggest three ways she could reduce heat loss through the windows of her new house.

1. ....

2. ....

3. ....

Q5 Mr Tarantino wants to buy **double glazing** for his house, but the salesman tries to sell him insulated window shutters instead. He says it is cheaper and more **cost-effective**.

	Double glazing	Insulated window shutters
Initial Cost	£3000	£1200
Annual Saving	£60	£20
Payback time	50 years	

a) Calculate the **payback time** for insulated shutters and write it in the table.

b) Is the salesman's advice correct? Give reasons for your answer.

....

....

Efficiency

Q1 Tick the boxes to show whether these statements are **true** or **false**.

		True	False
a)	The **total energy supplied** to a machine is called the **input**.	☐	☐
b)	The **useful output** of a machine is never more than its total input.	☐	☐
c)	The **energy output** of a machine is the **useful energy** it delivers.	☐	☐
d)	The more **efficient** a machine is, the more energy it **wastes**.	☐	☐

Q2 Complete the following **energy transfer diagrams** to show the **useful** energy output of various devices. The first one has been done for you.

A **solar water heating panel**: .... light energy .... $\rightarrow$ .... heat energy ....

a) A gas cooker: .... $\rightarrow$ .... heat energy ....

b) A television screen : .... electrical energy .... $\rightarrow$ ....

c) An electric buzzer: .... $\rightarrow$ ....

Q3 Use the **efficiency formula** to complete the table.

Efficiency = Useful Energy Output ÷ Energy Input

Total Energy Input (J)	Useful Energy Output (J)	Efficiency
2000	1500	
	2000	0.50
4000		0.25
600	200	

Q4 Here is the **energy flow diagram** for an electric lamp. Complete the sentences below.

energy input 100 J → light energy output 5 J / heat energy output

a) The total **energy input** is .... J

b) The **useful energy output** is .... J

c) The amount of energy **wasted** is .... J

d) The efficiency of the bulb is .... J

Q5 Tina was investigating a model **winch** — a machine that uses an electric motor to lift objects.

Tina calculated that, in theory, **10 J** of electrical energy would be needed to lift a **boot** 50 cm off a table. She then tried lifting the boot with the winch and found that **20 J** of electrical energy was used.

Why did the winch use so much electrical energy in practice? In your answer, include an explanation of what happened to the 'extra' 10 joules.

....

....

Electromagnetic Waves

Q1 Diagrams A, B and C represent electromagnetic waves.

A   **B**   **C**

a) Which two diagrams show waves with the same **frequency**? ...... and ......

b) Which two diagrams show waves with the same **amplitude**? ...... and ......

c) Which two diagrams show waves with the same **wavelength**? ...... and ......

Q2 Indicate whether the following statements are true or false.

True False

a) Visible light travels faster in a vacuum than both X-rays and radio waves. ☐ ☐

b) All EM waves transfer matter from place to place. ☐ ☐

c) Radio waves have the shortest wavelength of all EM waves. ☐ ☐

d) All EM waves can travel through space. ☐ ☐

Q3 All EM waves can be **reflected**, **refracted** and **diffracted**.
Draw lines to match each of these three statements to the correct description.

a) Long-wave radio waves can bend around **obstacles** such as houses.

Reflection

b) Your remote control will still work if you point it away from the TV
towards a flat solid object, e.g. a wall.

Diffraction

c) The bottom of a swimming pool looks **nearer** than it actually is.

Refraction

Q4 EM radiation occurs at many different wavelengths.

Complete the table to show the seven types of EM waves:

			VISIBLE LIGHT			
1m-10^{4}m	10^{-2}m (3cm)	10^{-5}m (0.01mm)	10^{-7}m	10^{-8}m	10^{-10}m	10^{-12}m

Q5 EM waves with higher frequencies are generally more damaging. Explain, in terms of
wavelength and frequency, why some **ultraviolet** radiation can be almost as damaging as **X-rays**.

....

....

Module P1 — Energy for the Home

Wireless Communication

Q1 Fill in the gaps in this passage using the words supplied.

bounced quickly reflection short ionosphere slowly ionises refraction diffraction

Ultraviolet radiation from the Sun .... some of the atoms high in the atmosphere,

forming a layer known as the .... When a radio wave with a medium wavelength

meets this layer of charged particles it travels more .... and its direction is changed.

This is known as .... The radio wave is .... back to Earth. In this

way, radio waves can be made to travel longer distances than ....-wave signals.

Q2 Only some of these statements are true. Circle their letters.

A Long waves such as radio waves are good for transmitting information long distances.

B Some wavelengths of radio wave are refracted by the ionosphere and come back to Earth.

C When a wave meets a medium with a different density it can change direction.
This is known as interference.

Q3 Diagrams A and B show waves travelling from a **less dense** medium to a **denser** medium.

a) Which diagram shows the waves being **refracted**? ....

b) Why does refraction **not happen** in the other diagram?

....

c) What happens to the **wavelength** of the waves as they pass into the denser medium?

....

d) What happens to the **frequency** of the waves as they pass into the denser medium?

....

e) What happens to the **velocity** of the waves as they pass into the denser medium?

....

f) Imagine that the wave in the denser medium in diagram B passes into a **less dense** medium again. What would you expect to happen to the wave?

Think about wavelength, frequency and speed.

....

....

Wireless Communication

Q4   The diagram shows two different radio waves **A** and **B** being transmitted and received from **radio masts** on the Earth. Both waves have the same frequency.

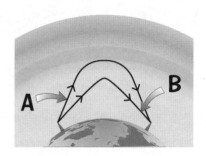

a)   Which of the waves is transmitted at a **higher angle of elevation**?

....

b)   What effect does the **angle of elevation** have on the **speed** at which information is received at the second mast?

....

....

c)   What kind of behaviour does the wave show when it meets the ionosphere and comes back to Earth? **Circle** the correct answer.

Reflection   **Refraction**   **Diffusion**   **Diffraction**

Diffraction —
Niiiiiice,
Groovy, man

Q5   When radio waves meet they **interfere** with one another. Interference can be constructive or destructive.

a)   The diagram below shows two waves combining. On each of the empty sets of axes, draw what the combined wave would look like.

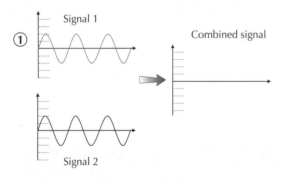

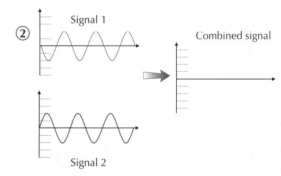

b)   Complete the following sentence to state the conditions needed to get complete destructive interference between two waves.

For two waves to completely destructively interfere, they must have the same amplitude,

the same .... and be completely .... phase.

c)   Rebekah listens to a radio station broadcasting on 1152 kHz. One day, another radio station starts broadcasting on 1155 kHz. Suggest why Rebekah's listening experience might be **worse** than before.

....

....

Top Tips: Remember that refraction is when a wave **changes direction** as it moves from one kind of stuff into another kind of stuff, at an angle. Without it, radio communication would be harder.

Module P1 — Energy for the Home

Wireless Communication and Ovens

Q1 **Waves spread out** when they pass through a gap, or go past an object.

a) What is the **technical name** for this spreading out?

....

b) How does the **size** of the gap a wave passes through affect the **amount** that it spreads out?

....

Q2 Tick to show which of the following statements are **true**.
Write out a correct version of any false statements.

True

a) Waves diffract most when they pass through a gap
the same size as their wavelength. ☐

b) Microwaves can diffract around large obstacles such as a large block of flats. ☐

c) Microwaves used for communication are absorbed by
the watery atmosphere before they can reach a satellite. ☐

d) Long wavelength waves are diffracted more than short ones. ☐

e) Microwaves can be diffracted by the edge of a transmission dish.
This spreads the signal out and makes it weaker. ☐

....

....

....

....

Q3 Sharon is heating up some **ready-made curry** in her **microwave** oven.

a) Briefly explain how microwaves heat up the curry.

....

....

b) The instructions on the curry packaging say to take the curry out of the microwave and **stir** it halfway through the cooking time. Sharon doesn't bother to do this. When she takes the curry out, it's **overcooked on top**, and **undercooked in the middle**. Explain in terms of heat transfer **why** the curry is like this.

....

....

....

Module P1 — Energy for the Home

Wireless Communication and Ovens

Q4 Gabrielle in London and Carwyn in Toronto are talking by **mobile phone**.

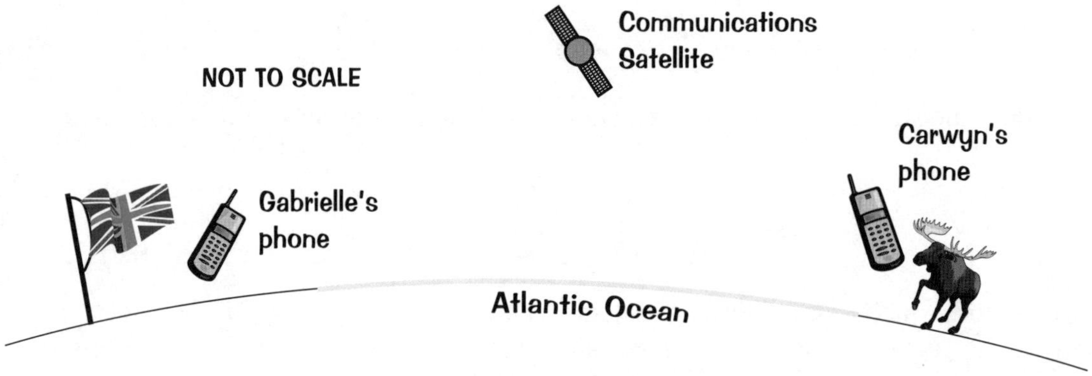

NOT TO SCALE

Communications Satellite

Carwyn's phone

Gabrielle's phone

Atlantic Ocean

a) Gabrielle's mobile phone sends a signal to a **transmitter**. The transmitter sends a signal to the communications satellite. Why **doesn't** Gabrielle's phone send the signal **straight to the satellite**?

....

b) Carwyn goes into the centre of Toronto, and finds that her mobile phone sometimes **loses reception** when she walks down streets with a lot of **tall buildings**.

i) Explain **why** Carwyn's phone loses reception in the city streets.

....

....

ii) The nearest transmitter to Carwyn is on a **hilltop** two miles from her house. Explain why the transmitter needs to be on a hilltop.

....

Q5 The diagram on the right shows a wave generator emitting some EM waves.

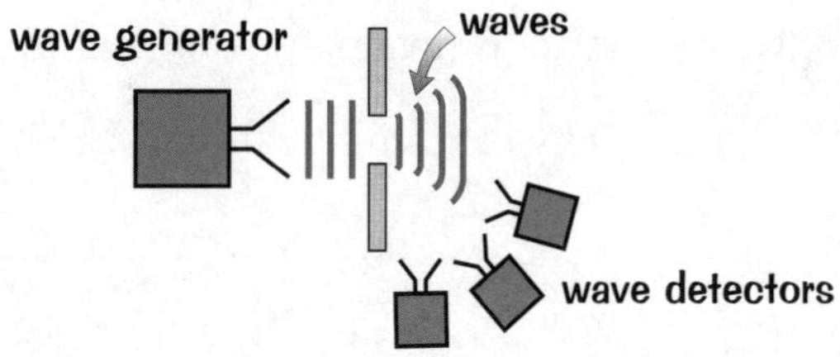

wave generator   waves

wave detectors

a) Describe how this apparatus could be used to find the **approximate length** of the waves being emitted.

....

....

....

b) Microwave ovens and mobile phones both use **microwave radiation**. Explain why your body does **not** get 'cooked' when you use a **mobile phone**.

....

....

Communicating with Light

Q1 Choose from the words below to complete the passage.

pulses	thousands	reflected	internal	diffraction	dense	core	infrared	gamma

Optical fibres depend upon total .... reflection for their operation. Visible

light or .... waves are sent down the cable and are ....

when they hit the boundary between the .... fibre and the less

.... outer layer. The signals travel as .... of light.

Each cable can carry .... of different signals.

Q2 Tick to show whether these statements are **true** or **false**. **True False**

a) Optical fibres send pulses of light or infrared radiation. ☐ ☐

b) Optical fibres work because the light signal is refracted along the fibre. ☐ ☐

c) For the signal to be transmitted, the rays must not enter the fibre at too sharp an angle. ☐ ☐

d) Optical fibre signals are subject to interference from other signals. ☐ ☐

Q3 The diagrams show rays of light in an **optical fibre**.
Draw arrows to match each diagram to the correct description of what is happening.

Total internal reflection

Most of the light passes out
of the optical fibre, but some
is reflected internally.

Most of the light is reflected
internally, but some emerges
along the surface of the glass.

Q4 Explain what is meant by the '**critical angle**' for a boundary between two materials.

....

....

Q5 **Radio** and **optical fibres** are two different ways of sending signals over long distances. Give two
advantages and one disadvantage of using optical fibres compared to radio to send information.

Advantages 1. ....

2. ....

Disadvantage ....

Digital Technology

Q1   Describe the main difference between **digital** and **analogue** signals.

....

....

Q2   Sketch: a 'clean' digital signal.   a 'noisy' digital signal.   a 'noisy' analogue signal.

Q3   Wendy listens to a radio talk show on a **digital radio** in her lounge. She then goes out
into the garden and listens to the same radio talk show on a **portable analogue radio**.

a)   The voices of the radio talk show host and their guests sound much **clearer**
on the **digital** radio than they do on the analogue radio. Explain why this is.

....

....

....

b)   Radio stations use **multiplexing** to digitally broadcast
their radio signals. Explain what 'multiplexing' means.

....

....

Q4   Digital signals have many advantages over analogue signals.

a)   Explain why digital signals suffer less from **noise** than analogue signals.

....

....

b)   State one other advantage of using digital signals for communication.

....

Digital Technology

Q5 The diagram shows how a **CD player** changes the pits on a CD into a signal which can be played through a loudspeaker.

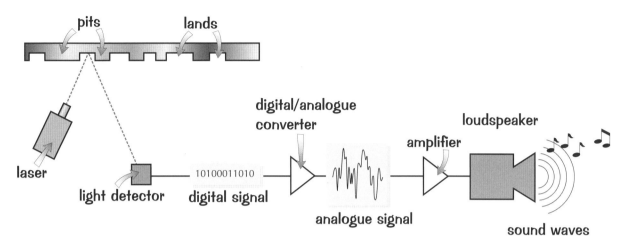

a) Why does the CD surface need to be **shiny**? ....

b) What happens to the laser light when it hits the **pit**?

....

c) How does the light sensor pick up the difference between **digital on**s **and off**s?

....

....

d) What is the function of the **amplifier**?

....

....

e) When a signal is amplified, random disturbances are added to the signal, lowering its quality.

   i) What are these random disturbances usually called? ....

   ii) Why does an analogue signal's quality decrease after amplification?

      ....

      ....

      ....

Top Tips: They don't expect you to know a **humungous** load about digital technology for the exam — good job really, because there's a lot of digital technology about these days. You will need to know **how a CD player works** and why digital signals don't suffer from **noise**, though.

Humans and the Environment

Q1 Prolonged exposure to the Sun is linked to an increased risk of **skin cancer**.

a) Which part of the radiation from the Sun causes the damage? ....

b) How are human cells affected by this radiation?

....

Q2 **Dark-skinned** people are better protected from harmful radiation than **fair-skinned** people.

a) **How** does dark skin give this protection?

....

b) Suggest two ways you can **reduce** your exposure to harmful radiation from the Sun.

1. ....

2. ....

c) Marie uses a sun cream with '**SPF 25**' on the label. What does 'SPF 25' mean?

....

Q3 The **ozone layer** helps protect life on Earth.

a) Where is the ozone layer? ....

b) **How** does the ozone layer help protect life on Earth?

....

c) Name one group of pollutant gases which break up ozone molecules.

....

Q4 Tick to show whether these statements are **true** or **false**.

		True	False
a)	A sun cream with an SPF of 15 protects you from harmful UV rays for 15 minutes.	☐	☐
b)	Buildings in a city absorb heat from the Sun during the day and emit it at night.	☐	☐
c)	Dust pollution can form a layer above a city and trap the heat in.	☐	☐

Q5 Human activity and natural events can cause **climate change**. State whether the following will increase or decrease the Earth's temperature. Explain your answers.

a) An erupting volcano. ....

....

b) Carbon dioxide emission. ....

....

Module P1 — Energy for the Home

Using the Wave Equation

Q1 Sea waves are coming towards a wall at a rate of a wave **every two seconds**.
The distance between one peak and the next is **two metres**.

a) What is the **frequency** of these waves? ....

b) Calculate the **velocity** of these waves. ....

Q2 A pebble is dropped into still water. Waves move out across the surface of the water.
The wavelength is **1.6 cm** and the waves are generated at a rate of **10 a second**.

a) What is the **frequency** of the waves in Hz? ....

b) Calculate the **speed** of the waves. ....

Be careful with <u>units</u>.

Q3 Radio waves travel at the **speed of light** (300 000 000 m/s).
Radio 3 has a **frequency** of **90 MHz**.

a) Write down the speed of light in **standard form**. ....

b) Write the **frequency** in Hz in standard form. ....

c) Calculate the **wavelength** of these radio waves. Give your answer in m.

....

Q4 The **upper limit** of human hearing is about **20 000 Hz**. Sound travels at 320 m/s in dry air.

a) What is the **wavelength** of the highest pitched sound that humans can hear?

....

b) The longest wavelength sound a loudspeaker makes has a wavelength of **16 metres**.
What is the **frequency** of this sound?

....

c) Approximately how many more times faster does light travel than sound in air?

....

Q5 The Sun is roughly **150 000 000 km** from the Earth.
Light takes about **8 minutes** to reach us from the Sun.

Watch out for <u>units</u>.

a) Use these figures to calculate a value for the **speed of light**.

....

....

b) A light wave has a wavelength of $\frac{1}{2000}$ mm. Use the value obtained in a) to calculate its frequency.

....

....

Seismic Waves

Q1 The diagram shows four layers of the Earth. Complete the table.

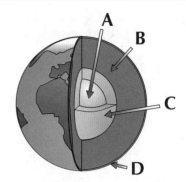

Layer	Name	Solid or liquid
A		
B		
C		
D		

Q2 Read the following sentences and underline the correct word from each highlighted pair.

Disturbances in the Earth produce **EM / seismic** waves which can travel **through / along** the Earth. These waves can be recorded on a seismograph, which draws a **seismologist / seismogram**.

Q3 Earthquakes can produce both **S waves** and **P waves**.

a) Which of these two types are **longitudinal** waves? ....

b) Which of these two types travels **faster**? ....

c) Which type of wave **cannot** travel through the **outer core** of the Earth? ....

Q4 Circle the letters next to any of these statements which are **true**.

A Both P and S waves can travel from the North Pole to the South Pole.

B A longitudinal wave travels in the same direction as the force which causes it.

C Transverse waves travel at right angles to the force which causes them.

D P waves travel more slowly through the inner core.
This suggests that it is made of solid material.

Q5 Both P and S waves **curve** as they travel through the Earth.

a) Why do they curve?

....

b) P waves can change direction abruptly as they travel through the Earth. Explain why this happens.

....

c) i) Which type of wave doesn't reach the opposite point of the Earth to the site of an earthquake?

....

ii) What does this tell seismologists about the structure of the Earth's interior?

....

Mixed Questions — Module P1

Q1   Ben sets up an experiment as shown.
He records the temperature readings on
thermometers A and B every two minutes.

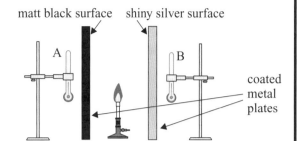

The graph below shows Ben's results
for thermometer **B**.

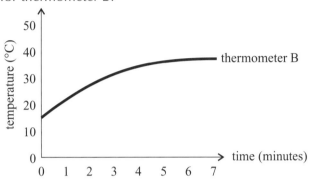

a)   On the diagram above, sketch the graph you would expect for thermometer **A**.

b)   Explain why the differences between the two graphs occur.

....

....

Q2   Steve has bought a new fridge-freezer.

a)   Steve's new fridge-freezer has its freezer compartment above the refrigerator.
How does this arrangement encourage **convection currents** in the main body of the fridge?

....

....

b)   Most fridges have a light which comes on when the door is opened. The light in Steve's new fridge
wastes 68 J of energy for every 100 J of useful output energy. Calculate the light's efficiency.

....

....

Q3   My landline telephone is connected to the telephone exchange by **optical fibres**.

a)   What **type** of EM wave might be sent from the exchange? ....

b)   Draw an annotated diagram to
show how an optical fibre works.

Mixed Questions — Module P1

Q4 Erik investigates ways of saving energy in his grandma's house. He calculates the annual savings that could be made on his grandma's fuel bills, and the cost of doing the work.

Work needed	Annual Saving (£)	Cost of work (£)
Hot water tank jacket	20	20
Draught-proofing	70	80
Cavity wall insulation	85	650
Thermostatic controls	30	140

a) Which of the options in the table would save Erik's grandma the most money **over 5 years**? Show your working.

....

....

....

b) Erik's grandma likes to have a hot bath in the evenings. How much energy is needed to heat 90 kg of water from 14 °C to 36 °C ? (The specific heat capacity of water is 4200 J/kg/°C.)

....

....

c) Erik goes on an Arctic expedition. He has to melt snow for drinking water. What mass of snow (at 0 °C) could he melt using the same amount of energy his grandma uses to heat her bath water? (The specific latent heat of water for melting is 334 000 J/kg.)

....

....

Q5 The diagram below shows the paths of some seismic waves travelling through the Earth.

a) Label the layers **i)** to **iv)** on the diagram.

b) All the waves whose paths are shown are of the same type. What type are they? Circle the correct answer.

    P waves   S waves

c) The waves curve gradually in layer **ii)** but change direction suddenly at the boundary between layers **ii)** and **iii)**. Explain why.

....

....

Mixed Questions — Module P1

Q6 Waves A, B and C represent **infrared**, **visible light** and **ultraviolet** radiation (not in that order). They are all drawn to the same scale.

a) Which of the waves has the greatest amplitude? ....

b) Which of the waves represents UV radiation? ....

c) Describe one way in which human activities have caused an increase in our exposure to UV radiation from sunlight.

....

....

d) Give an example of one **natural** event which might lead to a significant **decrease** in our exposure to radiation from the Sun. ....

Q7 Radio Roary transmits **long-wave** signals with a wavelength of **1.5 km**.

a) Calculate the **frequency** of Radio Roary's transmission. (Use speed = 3×10^8 m/s.)

....

....

b) Mr Potts is on holiday in the Scottish Highlands. The cottage he's staying in has a TV and radio. Mr Potts loves 'The Archers' on Radio 4, but finds that he can only get long-wave radio reception. TV reception is also very poor, so he can't watch his favourite cookery and gardening shows.

Explain why Mr Potts gets **good** long-wave radio reception, but such **poor** short-wave radio and TV reception.

....

....

c) Radio Piracy broadcasts at a frequency of 201 kHz. Both Radio Roary and Radio Piracy broadcast **analogue** signals.

  i) Why might Radio Piracy's frequency be a problem for people listening to these stations?

  ....

  ii) Suggest a way to reduce the problem without changing the frequency of the transmissions.

  ....

d) Mr Potts' holiday cottage has a microwave oven. The microwaves used in ovens are different from those used to carry mobile phone signals. Explain how they differ, and why different types are used.

....

....

Module P2 — Living for the Future

Using the Sun's Energy

Q1 Choose from the words below to complete the passage about how **solar cells** generate electricity. Each word may be used once, more than once, or not at all.

semiconductor   metal   atoms   neutrons   DC   protons   AC   electrons   silicon

Many solar cells are made of ...., which is a ....

When sunlight falls on the cell, silicon .... absorb some of the energy of the light, which knocks some of their .... loose. These .... then flow around a circuit to give a .... current.

Q2 The diagram shows a solar cell generating direct current (DC).

sunlight   solar cell   bulb   electric current (D.C.)

a) What is meant by **direct** current?

....

b) Explain how **sunlight intensity** and the **surface area** of a solar cell affect its electrical power output.

....

....

Q3 Solar cells can also be called **photovoltaic cells**.

a) Give two advantages of using photovoltaic cells to generate electricity.

1) ....

2) ....

b) Give one disadvantage of using photovoltaic cells to generate electricity.

....

Q4 The diagram shows a **passive solar heating panel**.

matt black water pipe   warm water out   glass box   cold water in

a) **i)** Why is the water pipe matt black?

....

ii) Why is the water pipe inside a glass box?

....

b) A solar panel can be made to track the position of the Sun in the sky. Why is this done?

....

Producing and Distributing Electricity

Q1 Complete the passage by choosing from the words given.

National	Express	Grid	power stations	worms	farms	consumers	generated

Most electricity is produced by .... The ....

.... is the network of pylons and cables which covers the whole country.

It enables electricity .... almost anywhere to be supplied to

.... almost anywhere, e.g. homes and ....

Q2 **Wind turbines** can be used to generate electricity from **moving air**.

What is the original source of the wind energy that turns the turbine?

What causes the air to move?

turbine blades

electrical output

generator

....

Q3 In a large **power station**, there are several steps involved in making electricity. Number these steps in the right order — from 1 to 5.

☐ Hot steam rushes through a turbine and makes it spin.

☐ Electricity is produced by the spinning generator.

☐ A fossil fuel such as coal is burned to release heat.

☐ The spinning turbine makes the generator spin too.

☐ Water is heated in the boiler and turned to steam.

Q4 Write the five **fuels** given below in the correct columns of the table to indicate their **fuel type**.

uranium

wood

oil   coal

natural gas

Fossil	Nuclear	Biomass

Q5 Both wood and coal produce **carbon dioxide** when they are burned.

a) Wood from fast-growing trees is a **renewable** resource. Explain what this means.

....

b) Explain why burning wood is 'carbon neutral' but burning coal is not.

....

....

....

The Dynamo Effect

Q1   Look at the apparatus shown in the diagram below.

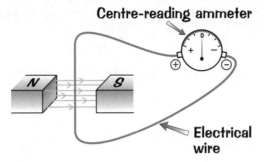

Centre-reading ammeter

An ammeter measures the flow of electric current.

Electromagnetic induction is sometimes called the *generator effect*.

Electrical wire

a)   Describe how you could use the apparatus to demonstrate electromagnetic induction.

....

....

....

b)   What you would see on the ammeter? ....

....

c)   What effect, if any, would the following have:

   i) swapping the magnets

   ....

   ii) reversing the connections to the ammeter

   ....

Q2   A simple **dynamo** can be made by rotating a magnet end to end inside a coil of wire.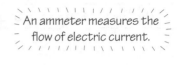

a)   What happens to the magnetic field when the magnet turns half a turn?

....

b)   What is created in the wire by this rotation?

....

c)   The magnet is constantly turned in the same direction.
   Would this generate an AC or DC current in the wire?

....

Q3   Explain why the lights on a bicycle with a dynamo **flicker** and go **dim** as the bicycle slows down.

....

....

The Dynamo Effect

Q4 Moving a **magnet** inside a **coil** of **copper wire** produces a trace on a cathode ray oscilloscope.

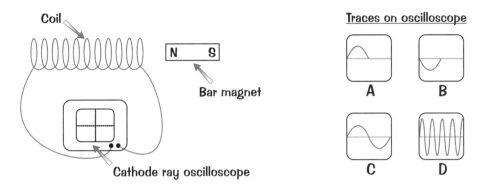

Coil

Bar magnet

Cathode ray oscilloscope

Traces on oscilloscope

A   B

C   D

When the magnet was pushed inside the coil, Trace A was produced on the screen.

a) Explain how Trace B could be produced.

....

b) Explain how Trace C could be produced.

....

c) Explain how Trace D could be produced.

....

d) Explain how energy is transferred from the moving magnet to the oscilloscope.

....

Q5 Look at the simple **AC generators** sketched below.

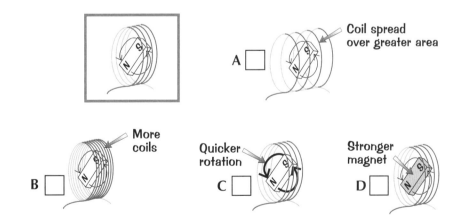

A ☐   Coil spread over greater area

B ☐   More coils

C ☐   Quicker rotation

D ☐   Stronger magnet

One of the generators labelled A - D will **not** induce a higher voltage
than the generator in the pink box. Tick the appropriate box.

> **Top Tips:** Electromagnetic induction is a very **useful** bit of Physics, because it's how we
> make all our electricity. The massive generators in a power station and the tiny whirring dynamo on
> my bike both work in the same way — there's a **conductor** experiencing a **changing magnetic field**,
> and the result is an **induced voltage**. In fact, with a few spare parts from a pedalo and some wire,
> you could set up a generator under your desk, pedal away all day and solve the UK's energy crisis.

Supplying Electricity Efficiently

Q1 Number these statements 1 to 5 to show the order of the steps that are needed to deliver energy to Mrs Miggins' house so that she can boil the kettle.

	An electrical current flows through power cables across the country.
	Mrs Miggins boils the kettle for tea.
	Electrical energy is generated in power stations.
	The voltage of the supply is raised.
	The voltage of the supply is reduced.

Q2 Each of the following sentences is incorrect. Write out a correct version of each.

a) The National Grid transmits energy at high voltage and high current.

....

b) A step-up transformer is used to reduce the voltage of the supply before electricity is transmitted.

....

c) Using a high current makes sure there is not much energy wasted.

....

Q3 Use the **efficiency formula** to complete the table.

Efficiency = Useful Energy Output ÷ Energy Input

Total Energy Input (J)	Useful Energy Output (J)	Efficiency
2000	1500	
	2000	0.50
4000		0.25

Q4 At full working speed a **generator** in a power station turns **50 times per second**.

a) What type of electrical current is supplied by the generator — **AC** or **DC**?

....

b) Explain how this type of current allows the voltage of the supply to be stepped up or down.

....

....

Q5 One litre of oil produces 6 MJ of energy when it is completely burned in air.
A power station with an overall efficiency of 30% consumes oil at the rate of 40 litres per second.
Calculate the **total energy loss per second** for the power station.

....

....

Module P2 — Living for the Future

Electrical Power

Q1   The **current** an appliance draws depends on its **power** rating. Complete the table below, showing the power rating and current drawn by various appliances at mains voltage — **230 V**.

Appliance	Power (W)	Current (A)
Kettle	2600	
Radio	13	
Laptop computer		3.2
Lamp		0.17

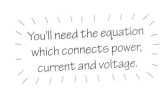
You'll need the equation which connects power, current and voltage.

Q2   Boris puts his **2 kW** electric heater on for 3 hours.

a)   Calculate how many **kilowatt-hours** of electrical energy the heater uses.

.... kWh.

b)   Boris gets his electricity supply from Ivasparkco. They charge 7p per kilowatt-hour. Work out the **cost** of the energy calculated in part (a).

....

....

c)   Boris's wife grumbles at him for leaving a 60 W lamp on overnight — about 9 hours every night. Boris says his wife uses **more energy** by using an 8 kW shower for 15 minutes every day.

Is Boris right? Calculate how much energy each person uses and compare your results.

....

....

....

Q3   Mr Havel recently received his **electricity bill**. Unfortunately, he tore off the bottom part to write a shopping list.

a)   How many **Units** of energy did Mr Havel use in the three months from June to September?

....

b)   What would the bill have said for 'total cost'?

....

....

Customer : Havel, V

Date   Meter Reading

11 06 06   34259
10 09 06   34783

Total Cost @ 9.7p per Unit

Electrical Power

Q4   **Off-peak electricity** is sometimes **cheaper** than electricity at peak times.

a)   Give an example of an electrical appliance designed to use off-peak electricity.

....

b)   i)   Give one advantage for the consumer of using off-peak electricity:

....

ii)   Give one advantage for the electricity generating company of using off-peak electricity:

....

....

Q5   **Pumped storage** power stations work by using **off-peak** electricity to pump water into a holding reservoir at night. In the daytime they release water from the reservoir to generate electricity, which is then sold to the National Grid at **peak rate** prices. The table below shows data for a typical pumped storage power station.

	Night time (input)	Daytime (output)
Running time	7 hours	5 hours
Power	275 MW	288 MW
Cost per kWh	3.7p	7.2p

Be careful — watch out for <u>units</u>.

a)   Calculate the cost of electricity used in the night time operation.

....

....

b)   Calculate the value (in £) of the electricity generated in the daytime operation.

....

....

Q6   A tumble drier operating on a **230 V household supply** uses a current of **10 A**.

a)   Calculate the power rating of the tumble drier in kW.

....

b)   Peak time electricity costs 11.3p/Unit. Off peak electricity costs 6.0p/Unit. Calculate the **money saved** if a tumble drier is operated for 2 hours during off peak hours rather than at peak time.

....

....

Power Sources for the Future

Q1   People often **object** to wind turbines being put up near to where they live.

   a)   Give two reasons why they might object to wind turbines.

      1) ....

      2) ....

   b)   Give two arguments in favour of using wind power.

      1) ....

      2) ....

Q2   Each of the following sentences is incorrect. Write a correct version of each.

   a)   A nuclear reactor uses radon to make heat.

      ....

   b)   Nuclear power stations are cheaper to build than coal-fired power stations and quicker to start up.

      ....

Q3   Outline three **disadvantages** of using nuclear power.

      1. ....

      2. ....

      3. ....

Q4   State one **advantage** of nuclear power over generating electricity from:

   a)   fossil fuels ....

   b)   renewable energy ....

Q5   Use the words and phrases below to complete the passage. Words may be used more than once.

control rods	fuel rods	plutonium	nuclear weapons	uranium

Used .... can be reprocessed.

Reprocessing produces more .... and some

.... The .... can be reused in the reactor

and the .... can be used to make ....

Nuclear Radiation

Q1 Complete the passage using the words given below. You will not have to use all the words.

ions   less   more   electrons   further   less far

When ionising radiation hits atoms it sometimes knocks ....

off the atoms, leaving behind .... Radiations which are more

ionising travel .... into a material and tend to cause

.... damage in the material they have penetrated.

Q2 Complete the table below by choosing the **correct word** from each column.

Radiation Type	Ionising power weak/moderate/ strong	Charge positive/none/ negative	Relative size no mass/ small/large	Penetrating power low/moderate/ high	Relative speed slow/fast/ very fast
alpha					
beta					
gamma					

Q3 a) For each sentence, tick the correct box to show whether it is **true** or **false**.

True False

i) Alpha and beta radiations are both deflected by magnetic fields. ☐ ☐

ii) Gamma radiation has no mass because it is an EM wave. ☐ ☐

iii) Alpha is the slowest and most strongly ionising type of nuclear radiation. ☐ ☐

iv) Beta particles are electrons, so they do not come from the nucleus. ☐ ☐

b) For each of the false sentences, write out a correct version.

....

....

....

Q4 Explain clearly why gamma rays are **less ionising** than alpha particles.

....

....

....

Nuclear Radiation

Q5 Brian was investigating three radioactive sources — A, B and C. Radiation from each source was directed through an **electric field** (between X and Y), towards target sheets of **paper**, **aluminium** and **lead**. Counters were used to detect where radiation passed through the target sheets.

Source A — the radiation was partially absorbed by the lead.
Source B — the radiation was deflected by the electric field, and stopped by the paper.
Source C — the radiation was deflected by the electric field, and stopped by the aluminium.

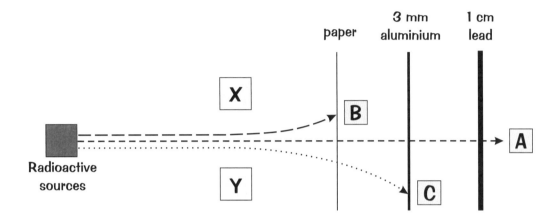

a) What type of radiation is emitted by:

source A? ...., source B? ...., source C? ....

b) Explain why radiation from source A is **not deflected** by the electric field.

....

....

c) What other type of **field** would deflect radiation from sources B and C?

....

d) After the experiment, Brian noticed that even when none of his radioactive sources were present, the counters still registered some radiation.

i) Explain why this was.

....

ii) Suggest how Brian should take account of this.

....

....

Top Tips: It's important to learn the **properties** of the different kinds of nuclear radiation — like whether they're stopped by lead or paper or aluminium. Get these questions right, and you'll be more likely to get the ones on the **next two pages** about practical uses of radiation right **as well**.

Uses of Nuclear Radiation

Q1   The following sentences explain how a **smoke detector** works, but they are in the wrong order.
Put them in order by labelling them 1 (first) to 6 (last).

☐ The circuit is broken so no current flows.

1 The radioactive source emits alpha particles.

☐ A current flows between the electrodes — the alarm stays off.

☐ The alarm sounds.

☐ The air between the electrodes is ionised by the alpha particles.

☐ A fire starts and smoke particles absorb the alpha radiation.

Assume that a fire starts a while after the smoke detector was installed.

Q2   The diagram shows how **beta radiation** can be used
in the control of paper thickness in a paper mill.

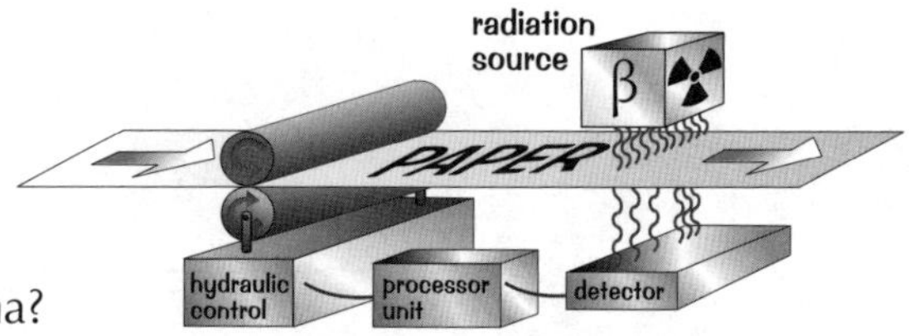

Why is beta radiation used, rather than alpha or gamma?

....

....

Q3   Radiation can be used to **sterilise** surgical instruments.

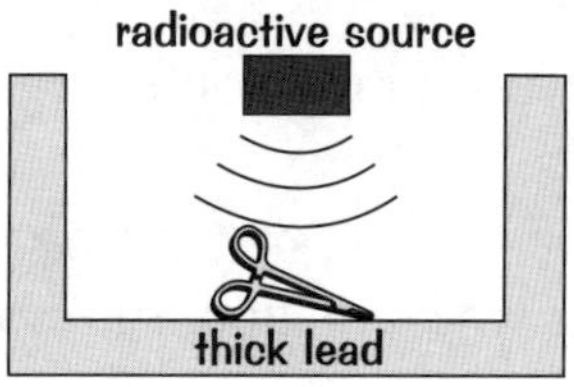

a)   What kind of radioactive source is used, and why?
In your answer, mention the **type** of radiation
emitted (α, β and γ) and the **half-life** of the source.

....

....

b)   What is the purpose of the thick lead?

....

c)   Similar machines can be used to treat fruit before it is exported from South America to Europe, to
stop it going bad on the long journey. How does irradiating the fruit help?

....

....

Q4   **Gamma radiation** can be used to test turbine blades in jet engines.

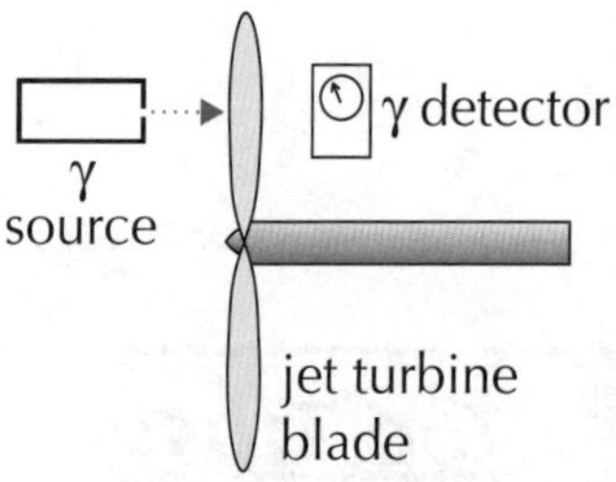

Explain how the test would detect a crack in the turbine blade.

....

....

....

Uses of Nuclear Radiation

Q5 Eviloilco knows that its oil pipeline is **leaking**, somewhere between points A and B.

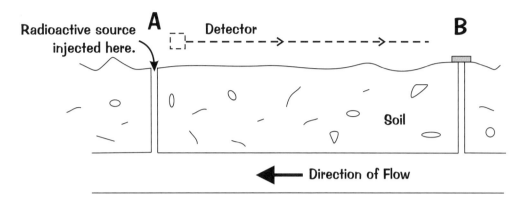

This is how Eviloilco plans to find the leak.

> We will inject a source of alpha radiation into the pipeline at point A. (This source has a long half-life — giving us better value for money in the long term.) After injecting the radioactive material, we will pass a sensor along the surface above the pipeline — and so detect where radiation is escaping, hence pinpointing the leak.

a) Give two reasons why Eviloilco has made a bad choice of radioactive source.

....

....

b) Even if they used the correct type of radioactive source, their plan would still fail. Why?

....

Q6 A patient has a **radioactive source** injected into her body to test her kidneys.

A healthy kidney will get rid of the radioactive material quickly (to the bladder). Damaged kidneys take longer to do this.

The results of the test, for both the patient's kidneys, are shown opposite.

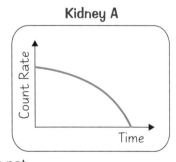

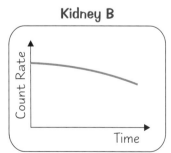

a) Explain how the doctor knew which kidney was working well and which was not.

....

b) Explain why an alpha source would **not** be suitable for this investigation.

....

....

Dangers from Radioactive Materials

Q1   Two scientists are discussing their samples of radioactive material.

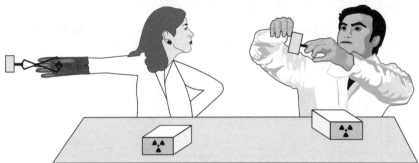

a)   One of the scientists is taking sensible safety precautions, but the other is not.
Describe three things which the careless scientist is doing wrong.

1) ....

2) ....

3) ....

b)   Describe another way the scientists can reduce their exposure to radiation,
besides using special apparatus or clothing.

....

c)   How should radioactive samples be stored when they are not in use?

....

Q2   In industry, sources of highly **penetrating** radiation
sometimes need to be **moved** from place to place.

a)   How can this be done without endangering the workers?

....

....

b)   Gamma radiation can pass easily through the walls of buildings.
How can workers in the surrounding areas be protected from this hazard?

....

....

Top Tips: You should always handle radioactive sources really carefully. People who work
with radioisotopes often wear **dosimeters** — badges which record their exposure. We're all exposed
to a low level of **background radiation** every day, though — from rocks etc. — and you can't do
anything about that (unless you fancy wearing a lead-lined suit and breathing apparatus all day long).

Dangers from Radioactive Materials

Q3 The diagram shows a worker in the nuclear industry mixing two **radioactive** powders.

Fill in the table describing the protective equipment and how each piece of equipment protects the worker from hazards. One has been done for you.

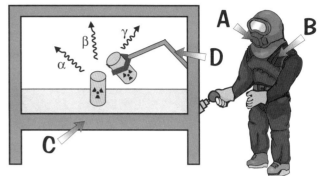

Equipment	Description	How it protects the worker
A	Air filter	Prevents inhalation of radioactive dust
B		
C		
D		

Q4 Hospitals and power stations produce **low-level nuclear waste**.

a) Give three examples of low-level nuclear waste.

1) ....

2) ....

3) ....

b) How is this low-level waste usually disposed of?

....

Q5 **High-level** radioactive waste is **harder** to dispose of than low-level waste.

a) For how long can high-level waste stay radioactive?

....

b) High level nuclear waste is disposed of by burying it deep underground.
What is often done to the waste before it's buried?

....

....

c) Scientists have to find suitable sites to bury high-level nuclear waste.
Why must sites for disposal of high-level waste be geologically stable?

....

....

Module P2 — Living for the Future

Earth's Magnetic Field

Q1   The diagram shows the Earth with an imaginary bar magnet inside it and its surrounding **magnetic field**.

Geographic .... pole.

.... pole of
the Earth's magnetic field

Geographic .... pole.

.... pole of
the Earth's magnetic field

compass

a)   Draw arrows on the dotted lines to show the direction of the Earth's magnetic field.

b)   Complete the labels at the Earth's poles with the words "north" and "south".

c)   Draw an arrow on the compass to show which direction its north pole would point.

Q2   It is thought that **electric currents** in the Earth's **core** create its magnetic field.

a)   What substance are these currents flowing in?

   ....

b)   In the lab, how could you create a magnetic field around a coil of wire?

   ....

c)   Sketch the shape of the magnetic field around this coil of wire.

⊕   ⊖

Q3   Jack's boat is in the Atlantic Ocean, **due south** of Ghana. Jack has a **small bar magnet** with its **north and south poles** marked on it and a piece of thin **string**.

Explain how Jack could use this equipment
to help set a course for Ghana.

   ....

   ....

   ....

Ghana

N

Jack

Earth's Magnetic Field

Q4 The diagram shows how a switch can be used to open a door lock which is then closed by a spring. The bolt that holds the door closed is a **bar magnet**.

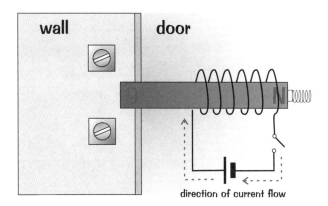

Describe what happens when the switch is closed, and why this makes the lock open.

....

....

....

Q5 The following diagrams show how scientists think the **Moon** was formed.

1) A small planet collided side-on with the Earth.

2) The iron cores of the planets fused at very high temperatures.

3) Low density bits flew off and orbited the Earth.

4) The bits eventually came together as the Moon.

Explain how the following facts about the Earth and the Moon support this theory.

a) The Moon is less dense than the Earth.

....

....

b) The Moon doesn't have a big iron core, but the Earth does.

....

....

c) The Moon is made of materials with high melting points and boiling points.

....

....

Particles and Rays from the Sun

Q1   As well as light, the Sun also emits **cosmic rays**, which are mainly **charged particles**.

   a)   Give one effect of these charged particles hitting gas particles in the Earth's atmosphere.

   ....

   b)   The Earth's magnetic field helps to shield us from cosmic rays.

   i)   Why are cosmic rays potentially harmful to living organisms?

   ....

   ii)   Explain **how** the Earth's magnetic field shields us from the charged particles in cosmic rays.

   ....

Q2   From time to time, massive explosions called **solar flares** happen on the surface of the Sun.

   What's emitted by solar flares that can disturb the Earth's magnetic field?

   ....

Q3   Artificial **satellites** can be affected by solar flares.

   a)   Give three uses of artificial satellites.

   ....

   ....

   b)   The electrical systems on satellites are sometimes shut down during solar flare activity. Why?

   ....

   ....

Q4   This diagram shows the Earth's **magnetic field**.

   a)   **What are** the polar lights (aurora borealis and aurora australis)?

   ....

   ....

   b)   What **causes** the polar lights?

   ....

   ....

The Solar System

Q1 This diagram shows the major bodies in the Solar System. It **isn't to scale**.

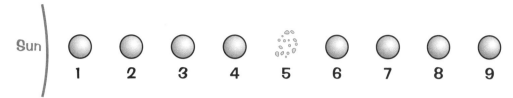

Sun 1 2 3 4 5 6 7 8 9

In the table below, write the correct number under each name
to show its position in the Solar System.

Body	Mars	Jupiter	Asteroids	Venus	Saturn	Neptune	Earth	Mercury	Uranus
Number									

Q2 When Robert looks up into the night sky,
he sees **stars** and **planets** (as long as it's a clear night).

Give three ways in which the planets that Robert sees
are different from the stars he sees.

1) ....

2) ....

3) ....

Q3 The planet **Venus** can be seen shining like a star in the evening sky.
It is sometimes called the Evening Star.

a) Does Venus emit its own light?

....

b) Draw lines on the diagram to show the path that light takes
to form an image of Venus in the evening sky on Earth.

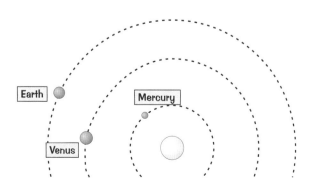

Earth

Mercury

Venus

The Solar System

Q4 The **Moon** orbits the **Earth** which is itself orbiting the **Sun** as shown. The diagram is not to scale.

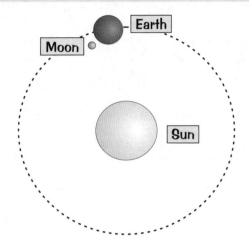

a) i) A force that causes circular motion acts in **which direction**?

....

ii) What is the name for this type of force? ....

b) Name the force which keeps the Earth and Moon in their orbits. ....

c) Draw an arrow on the diagram to show the direction of the force acting on the Earth which keeps it orbiting the Sun.

d) Explain why the Moon is not pulled away from the Earth by the Sun.

....

....

Q5 The diagram shows the Earth's orbit around the Sun.

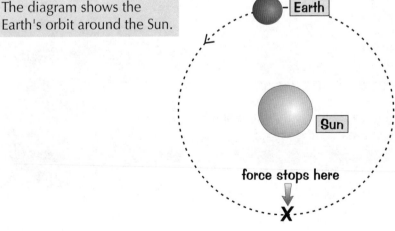

Draw an arrow to show how the Earth would move if the force holding it in orbit suddenly stopped acting when the Earth reached point X.

In what direction is the Earth moving at point X?

Top Tips: The hippies were wrong — it's not love that makes the world go round. Nor is it greed and it's certainly not oil. Ridiculous. It's **gravity**. GCSE Science is no place for metaphors.

Asteroids and Comets

Q1   As well as planets, there are **asteroids** orbiting the Sun.

a)   The asteroids orbit in the **asteroid belt**. This is between the orbits of which two planets?

.... and ....

b)   Roughly how big are the largest asteroids? Circle the correct diameter below.

  A 1000 mm   **B 1000 cm**   **C 1000 m**   **D 1000 km**

Q2   Choose from the words and phrases below to complete the passage.
Words can be used more than once.

meteorites	stars	asteroids	atmosphere	burn up	meteors	shooting

.... are rocks or dust that enter the Earth's atmosphere.

As they pass through the .... they .... and are seen

as .... Remains of the ....

that land on the Earth's surface are called ....

Q3   Scientists think that a very large **asteroid** struck the Earth at the Yucatán peninsula in the Gulf of Mexico about 65 million years ago and caused the **extinction** of over half the species on Earth.

a)   What **evidence** is there that asteroids have collided with the Earth?

....

....

b)   Explain how the asteroid's impact might have led to the extinction of so many species.

....

....

....

Q4   Some astronomers work on finding **Near Earth Objects**.

a)   What are Near Earth Objects?

....

b)   Explain why it is important to track their trajectories.

....

....

Asteroids and Comets

Q5 The diagram shows the orbit
of a **comet** around the Sun.

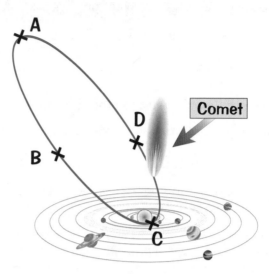

a) What is the name of the **shape** of the comet's orbit?

....

b) Write down the letters that show where the comet's speed is at its:

i) maximum: .... **ii)** minimum: ....

c) Explain your answers to part b).

....

....

d) **i)** What are comets made of? ....

ii) What causes the comet to have a 'tail'?

....

Q6 The asteroids in the asteroid belt haven't **clumped
together** to form a single planet, even though
each exerts a gravitational pull on the others.
Suggest why they **haven't** formed a single planet.

*Think about the sizes of the
planets — especially the planets
nearest to the asteroids.*

....

....

....

Top Tips: Don't get asteroids and comets mixed up. Asteroids stay in the asteroid belt
where they belong (well, they do most of the time), and comets have really long orbits that take them
even further out than the furthest planets, and really close in to the Sun.

Beyond the Solar System

Q1   One of the following statements is **not true**. Circle the letter next to the false statement.

    A A galaxy is made up of billions of stars.

    B The distance between galaxies can be millions of times the distance between stars.

    C Gravity is the force which keeps stars apart.

    D Galaxies rotate in space.

    E Planets are formed from the same clouds of gas and dust as stars.

Q2   The **light year** is used as a unit of length by astronomers.

  a)   Write down a definition of a light year.

....

  b)   Calculate the length **in km** of one **light year** given that:

      1 day = 24 hours

      1 year = 365.25 days

      Speed of light = 3×10^8 m/s.

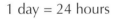

Watch out for units — the answer has to be in <u>km</u>, not <u>m</u>.

....

....

  c)   The Milky Way is about 100 000 light years in diameter. The Solar System is about halfway along one of the Galaxy's spiral arms. Use your answer to part b) to calculate how far we are from the centre of the Galaxy, in **km**, giving your answer in standard form, to 3 significant figures.

....

....

Q3   **Black holes** are the last stages in the lives of big stars.

  a)   Explain in terms of gravity why black holes are black.

....

....

....

  b)   How do scientists detect black holes?

....

....

Exploring the Solar System

Q1   Scientists estimate that a round trip to **Mars** would take astronauts up to **2 years** to complete.
Identify four problems associated with such a journey.

1) ....

2) ....

3) ....

4) ....

Q2   Scientists have already landed **unmanned probes** on Mars.

a)   Outline two advantages of using unmanned probes.

....

....

b)   Describe one disadvantage of using unmanned probes.

....

Q3   Not all unmanned probes are designed to land on a body's surface.

a)   What kinds of data can be collected **without** landing on the surface?

....

....

b)   Probes designed to land safely on the surface often carry exploration **rovers**
which can explore their surroundings and collect data.

i)   What kinds of investigation could be carried out by an exploration rover?

....

....

ii)   Several probes intended to land on Mars have failed — they've been damaged
too badly to work. Suggest why it is so difficult to land a probe safely.

....

....

....

The Origin of the Universe

Q1 The Big Bang theory is the accepted scientific explanation for the origin of the Universe.

a) Complete this passage using the words supplied below.

expansion	matter	energy	expand	age	explosion

Many scientists believe that the universe started with all the

............................and .... in one small space. There

was a huge .... and the material started to

.... Scientists can estimate the .... of

the universe using the current rate of ....

b) Why are estimates of the age of the Universe quite **unreliable**?

....

Q2 Francesca is standing by a busy street when an ambulance rushes past, sirens blaring.

As the ambulance moves away, how will the siren sound different to Francesca?
Underline the correct answer.

It will sound higher pitched   **It will sound lower pitched**

Q3 Brian set up a microphone at his local railway station to record his favourite **train noises**.
He attached the microphone to an oscilloscope.

An express train passed through the station at a constant speed. Diagram A below shows the trace on the monitor at 11:31:07, as the train **approached** Brian's microphone.

On diagram B, sketch the trace Brian might have seen as the train **left** the station.

A

11:31:07

B

11:31:08

Q4 What **evidence** is there to support the idea that the Universe began with a 'Big Bang'?
Include a brief explanation of **red-shift** and **cosmic background radiation** in your answer.

....

....

....

....

....

The Life Cycle of Stars

Q1   A star in its **stable** phase **doesn't get bigger or smaller**, even though there are forces tending to make it expand and forces trying to make it contract.

   a)   What causes the outward pressure on the star?

....

   b)   What is the force pulling the star inwards? ....

   c)   Why doesn't the star expand or contract?

....

   d)   What is another name for a star in its stable phase? ....

Q2   Stars are formed from clouds of dust and gas.

   a)   **Why** does the material come together?

....

   b)   Where does the **heat and light energy** emitted by a star come from?

....

Q3   Old stars eventually turn into **red giants**.

   a)   What causes a star to become a red giant? ....

....

   b)   Why is a red giant red? ....

Marilyn was nearing the
end of her stable phase

....

Q4   Complete the passage below to describe what eventually happens to red giants.

A small star will eject gas and dust as a ....,
leaving a dense core called a .... A bigger star
will explode as a ...., leaving a very dense core
called a .... The biggest stars form
.... instead.

Due to printing
restrictions, red
giants are currently
unavailable.

Q5   Explain what happens in a big star **as it changes** from a red giant to a supernova.

....

....

Mixed Questions — Module P2

Q1 Electricity is generated in **power stations** and reaches our homes by a network of **power cables**.

a) In a gas-fired power station, gas is burned and its chemical energy is converted into heat energy.

i) Describe how this heat energy is then converted into electrical energy.

....

ii) If a power station is 38% efficient, how much energy is **wasted** for every 1000 J of electrical energy **produced**?

....

iii) Where did the chemical energy in natural gas **originally** come from? Explain your answer.

....

....

b) Natural gas is a fossil fuel. Burning it releases carbon dioxide and contributes to climate change.

i) Suggest two alternative types of fuel which could be used to produce heat in power stations without contributing to climate change.

.... and ....

ii) It is now possible to install solar cells and wind turbines on the roof of a house. Explain why few households in the UK could rely on these technologies for their electricity supply.

....

....

c) **i)** Explain why electricity transmission cables are at very high voltages.

....

ii) Explain why the high voltage of the cables is not dangerous for people using the electricity.

....

Q2 The diagram represents a **light wave** emitted from Cygnus A — a galaxy about 700 million light years from Earth.

a) On the diagram, redraw the wave to show how it might appear to us on Earth because the light is **red-shifted**.

b) Explain how red-shifts from distant and nearer galaxies provide evidence for the Big Bang theory.

....

....

....

Module P2 — Living for the Future

Mixed Questions — Module P2

Q3 Jemima is using an **electric sander** which has a power rating of **360 W**.

a) The electricity supply in Jemima's house is at 230 V. Calculate the **current** the sander draws.

....

b) Jemima's electricity supplier charges **15.2p per kWh**. Jemima has the sander on for 45 minutes. How much does this cost (to the nearest penny)?

....

....

Q4 The table gives information about four different **radioisotopes**.

Source	Type of Radiation	Rate of Decay
radon-222	alpha	fast
technetium-99m	gamma	very fast
americium-241	alpha	very slow
cobalt-60	beta and gamma	slow

a) Explain which of these sources you would use, and why, in:

i) a smoke detector

....

....

ii) a medical tracer

....

....

b) Gamma radiation from cobalt-60 is used to test metal turbine blades for faults. What precautions should be taken by workers handling **cobalt-60**?

....

....

Q5 The diagram shows a **bicycle dynamo**. It is connected to a lamp (not shown).

a) When the knob is rotated clockwise at a constant speed, the lamp lights up. Explain why.

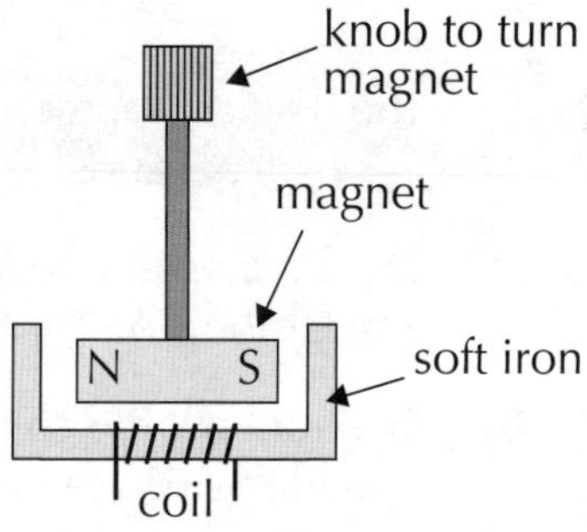

....

....

....

knob to turn magnet

magnet

N S

soft iron

coil

b) What difference would you notice if the magnet was rotated:

i) anticlockwise? ....

ii) faster? ....

Mixed Questions — Module P2

Q6 The Sun consists mainly of **hydrogen**. It also contains **helium**.

a) In a few million years time, the Sun will contain **more helium** and **less hydrogen** than it does now. Explain why.

....

....

b) The Sun is currently in its 'stable period'. What determines how long a star's stable period lasts?

....

c) Will the Sun ever become a **black hole**? Explain your answer.

....

Q7 The Earth's core contains **molten iron**. If the core were entirely **solid** there would probably be no 'northern lights'. Explain why.

....

....

....

Q8 As well as the planets, there are also **asteroids** and **comets** orbiting the Sun.

a) Explain what asteroids are and why they can pose a threat to life on Earth.

....

....

b) Why do comets **speed up** as they get closer to the Sun?

....

Q9 Exploring space is expensive and dangerous.

a) Name the ninth furthest planet from the Sun. ....

b) Explain why it is unlikely that a manned mission will be sent to this planet in the near future.

....

....

....

....

Speed and Acceleration

Q1   Ealing is about 12 km west of Marble Arch. It takes a
tube train 20 minutes to get to Marble Arch from Ealing.

Circle the letter next to the **true** statement below.

A The average speed of the train is 60 m/s.

B The average speed of the train is 10 m/s.

C The average speed of the train is 60 m/s due east.

D The average speed of the train is 36 m/s.

Albert
Square   Marble
Arch

Ealing   Walford
East

Q2   A pulse of laser light takes 1.3 seconds to travel from the Moon to the Earth.

If the speed of light is 3×10^8 m/s, how far away is the Moon from the Earth in km?

....

....

You'll need to
rearrange the
speed formula.

Q3   I rode my bike 1500 m to the shops. It took me 5 minutes.

a)   What was my average speed in m/s?

....

b)   One part of the journey was downhill and I averaged 15 m/s over this
300 m stretch. How long did it take to cover this bit of the journey?

....

c)   Going home I took a different route and my average speed was 4 m/s. It took me 8 minutes.
How far is the journey home?

....

....

Q4   The speed limit for cars on the motorway is 70 mph (about 31 m/s). A motorist accelerated onto
the motorway from a service station and was captured on a speed camera. He denied speeding.

Look at his **distance-time** graph.
Was the motorist telling the truth?

....

....

Think... you need to find the speed
from a distance-time graph.

Distance (m)

72
60
48
36
24
12
0

0.5   1.0   1.5   2.0   2.5   3.0

Time (s)

Speed and Acceleration

Q5 Steve walked to football training only to find that he'd left his boots at home.
He turned round and walked back home, where he spent 30 seconds looking for
them. To make it to training on time he had to run back at twice his walking speed.

Below is an incomplete **distance-time graph** for his journey.

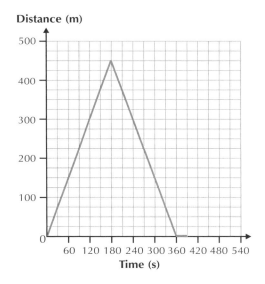

a) How long did it take Steve to walk to training?

....

b) Calculate Steve's speed for the first section of
the graph in m/s.

....

c) Complete the graph to show Steve's run back.

Q6 The graph shows the motion of a train as it travels from Alphaville
to Charlietown, where it stops briefly, and then moves off again.

a) Describe the motion of the train in the sections marked:

A ....

B ....

C ....

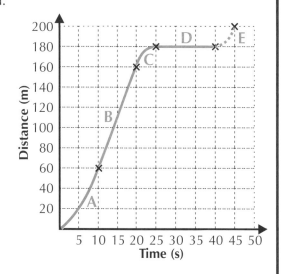

b) What is the train's **average** speed between
Alphaville and Charlietown?

....

....

c) Calculate the **maximum** speed of the train between the two stations.

....

d) How long does the train stop at Charlietown?

....

Speed and Acceleration

Q7   The Go Go car company make gas-powered model cars.
One car accelerates from rest to 20 m/s in 3.5 s.

a)   What is its acceleration?

....

b)   The car is modified and now accelerates from 3 m/s to 20 m/s in 2.8 s.
Show that this modification has improved the car's acceleration.

....

....

Q8   An egg is dropped from the top of the Eiffel tower.
It hits the ground after 8 seconds, at a speed of 80 m/s.

a)   Find the egg's acceleration. ....

b)   How long did it take for the egg to reach 40 m/s?

....

Q9   A car accelerates at 2 m/s². After 4 seconds it reaches a speed of 24 m/s.

How fast was it going before it started to accelerate?

....

....

Q10   Below is a speed-time graph for the descent of a lunar lander.
It accelerates due to the pull of gravity from the Moon.

Use the graph to calculate this acceleration.

....

....

....

Module P3 — Forces for Transport

Speed and Acceleration

Q11 The graph on the right shows a speed-skater's performance during a race.

a) How far does the skater go in the following sections:

X? ....

....

Y? ....

....

Z? ....

....

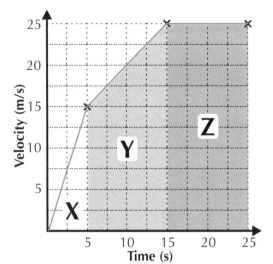

b) If the race finishes after 25 s, how far will she have travelled altogether?

....

Q12 Match each line on the distance-time graph with the correct line on the velocity-time graph.

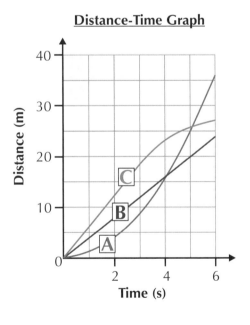

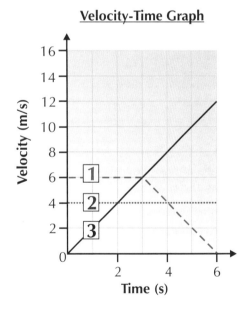

Line **A** = Line ....

Line **B** = Line ....

Line **C** = Line ....

Top Tips:

The most confusing thing about acceleration can be interpreting the graphs. The key thing to remember on a V-T graph is that the steepness of the line is the acceleration. If the line is curved, the acceleration is changing — the steeper the line, the greater the acceleration. Learn these facts and the graphs won't just look like a bunch of lines — they'll look like lines... but with meaning.

56

Forces

Q1 A teapot sits on a table.

a) Explain why it doesn't sink into the table.

....

b) Jane picks up the teapot and hangs it from the ceiling by a rope. What vertical forces now act on the teapot?

....

c) The rope breaks and the teapot accelerates towards the floor.

i) Are the vertical forces balanced? ....

ii) The teapot hits the floor without breaking and bounces upwards. Which force causes the teapot to bounce upwards?

....

Q2 A bear rides a bike north at a constant speed.

....

a) Label the forces acting on the bear.

b) The bear brakes and slows down. Are the forces balanced **as** he slows down? If not, which direction is the overall force in?

....

....

....

Q3 Khaleeda helps Jenny investigate falling objects. Jenny lets go of a tennis ball and Khaleeda times how long it takes to fall. Khaleeda draws the distance-time graph — it looks like the one shown.

Which phrase below describes points X, Y and Z? Explain what feature of the graph allows you to tell.

forces in balance   **reaction force from ground acts**

unbalanced force of gravity

What does the gradient of a distance-time graph tell you?

X: ....

You can tell this because ....

Y: .... You can tell this because:

....

Z: .... You can tell this because:

....

Friction Forces and Terminal Speed

Q1 Use the words supplied to fill in the blanks in the paragraph below about a sky-diver.

decelerates decrease less balances increase constant greater accelerates
When a sky-diver jumps out of a plane, his weight is .... than his air resistance, so he .... downwards. This causes his air resistance to .... until it .... his weight. At this point, his velocity is .... When his parachute opens, his air resistance is .... than his weight, so he .... This causes his air resistance to .... until it .... his weight. Then his velocity is .... once again.

Q2 Which of the following will **not** reduce the drag force on an aeroplane?
Tick the appropriate box.

☐ flying higher (where the air is thinner)   ☐ carrying less cargo

☐ flying more slowly   ☐ making the plane more streamlined

Q3 A scientist is investigating gravity by dropping a hammer and a feather.
Comment on the following predictions and explanations of what will happen.

a) "They will land at the same time — gravity is the same for both."

....

....

b) "The feather will reach its terminal velocity before the hammer."

....

....

Q4 You're investigating drag by dropping balls into a measuring cylinder full of oil and timing how long they take to reach the bottom. You have a golf ball, a glass marble and a ball bearing.

From this experiment, can you make any conclusions about the effect of size on drag?
Explain your answer.

....

....

....

Friction Forces and Terminal Speed

Q5   Explain what is meant when an object is described as streamlined.

....

....

Q6   Simon wants to test different lubricants by sliding a heavy block across a board covered in different substances. He measures how much force is required to get the block moving.

Surface substance	Force needed to get block moving (N)
Banana skins	40
Grease	36
Oil	30
Water	38

a)   **i)**   What is the maximum value of the static friction for water?

....

ii)   Suggest why oil is used as a lubricant.

....

b)   Simon does a similar experiment with a toy boat in a swimming pool.
He measures the force required to keep the boat moving at different speeds.

To keep the boat moving at a higher speed, what would need to happen to the force?

....

Q7   The graph shows how the velocity of a sky-diver changes before and after he opens his parachute.

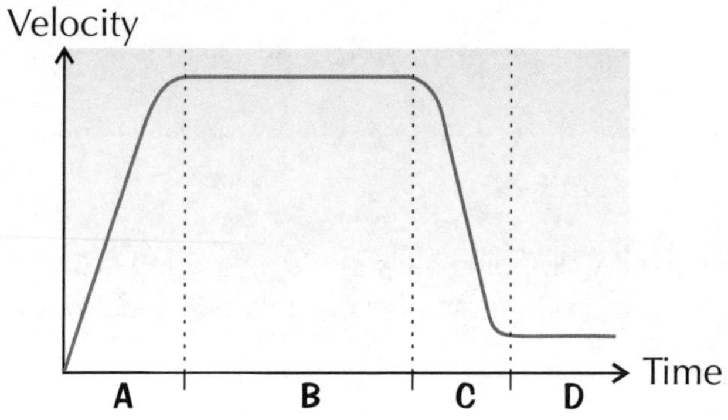

For each of the four regions A-D say whether the force of **weight** or **air resistance** is greater, or if they are **equal**.

Region A: ....   Region B: ....

Region C: ....   Region D: ....

Forces and Acceleration

Q1 Use the words supplied to fill in the blanks. You may need to use some words more than once.

proportional	force	reaction	stationary	accelerates	opposite
	constant	resultant	inversely	balanced	

If the forces on an object are .... , it's either .... or

moving at .... speed.

If an object has a .... force acting on it, it .... in the

direction of the .... The acceleration is .... to the force

and .... to its mass.

For every action there is an equal and ....

Q2 You're travelling home from school on a bus doing a steady speed in a straight line.
Which of the following is true? Tick the appropriate box.

☐ The driving force of the engine is bigger than friction and air resistance combined.

☐ There are no forces acting on the bus.

☐ The driving force of the engine is equal to friction and air resistance combined.

☐ No force is required to keep the bus moving.

Q3 State whether or not the forces acting on the following items are **balanced**,
and explain your reasoning.

a) A cricket ball slowing down as it rolls along the outfield.

....

b) A car going round a roundabout at a steady 30 mph.

....

c) A vase knocked off a window ledge.

....

d) A satellite orbiting over a fixed point on the Earth's surface.

....

e) A bag of rubbish ejected from a spacecraft in deep space.

....

Forces and Acceleration

Q4 Put these cars in order of increasing driving force.

Car	Mass (kg)	Maximum acceleration (m/s²)
Disraeli 9000	800	5
Palmerston 6i	1560	0.7
Heath TT	950	3
Asquith 380	790	2

1. ....

2. ....

3. ....

4. ....

Q5 Jo and Brian have fitted both their scooters with the same engine. Brian and his scooter have a combined mass of 110 kg and an acceleration of 2.80 m/s². On her scooter, Jo only manages an acceleration of 1.71 m/s².

  a) What **force** can the engine exert?

....

  b) Calculate the combined mass of Jo and her scooter.

....

Q6 Tom drags a 1 kg mass along a table with a newton-meter so that it accelerates at 0.25 m/s². If the newton-meter reads 0.4 N, what's the force of friction between the mass and the table?

....

....

Q7 A car tows a caravan along a road. At a constant speed, the pulling force of the car and the opposing reaction force of the caravan are equal. Which statement correctly describes the forces between the caravan and the car when the car accelerates? Tick the appropriate box.

☐ "The caravan's reaction force cancels out the pulling force of the car, so the caravan won't accelerate."

☐ "The caravan's reaction force is at a right angle to the force pulling the car, so the two forces don't affect one another."

☐ "The car's pulling force accelerates the caravan. The caravan's reaction acts on the car, not the caravan."

Q8 Which picture shows the weight (w) and reaction force (R) of a car on a slope? Tick the appropriate box.

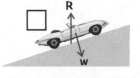 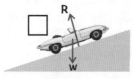 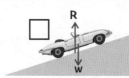 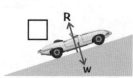

Forces and Acceleration

Q9   Which of the following statements correctly explains what happens when you walk?
Tick the appropriate box.

☐ Your feet push backwards on the ground, so the ground pushes you forwards.

☐ The force in your muscles overcomes the friction between your feet and the ground.

☐ The ground's reaction can't push you backwards because of friction.

☐ Your feet push forwards, and the ground's reaction is upwards.

Q10   A camper van with a mass of 2500 kg has a maximum driving force of 2650 N. It is
driven along a straight, level road at a constant speed of 90 kilometres per hour. At this
speed, air resistance is 2000 N and the friction between the tyres and the road is 500 N.

a)   **i)**   What force is the engine exerting? ....

   ii)   Complete the diagram to show all the forces acting on the camper van.
Give the size of each force.

b)   A strong headwind begins blowing, with a force of **200 N**. The van slows down.
Calculate its deceleration.

....

c)   The driver notices that the van is slowing and puts his foot right down on the accelerator,
applying the maximum driving force. How does the acceleration of the camper van change?
(Assume that air resistance and friction remain at their previous values.)

....

....

....

> **Top Tips:**   A resultant force means your object will accelerate — it will change its speed or
> direction (or both). But if your object has a constant speed (which could be zero) and a constant
> direction, you can say with utter confidence that there ain't any resultant force. Be careful though —
> a zero resultant force doesn't mean there are **no** forces, just that they all balance each other out.

Stopping Distances

Q1   A car driver's reaction time is 0.7 s. How far will the car go before the brakes are applied in an emergency, if it is travelling at 20 m/s? Tick the box next to the correct answer.

☐ 0.7 m   ☐ 14 m   ☐ 20 m   ☐ 28.6 m

Q2   The distance a car takes to stop is divided into: i) thinking distance and ii) braking distance.

a)   Explain what the thinking distance is for a driver.

....

b)   Why does a tired driver have a greater thinking distance?

....

Q3   Indicate whether the following statements are **true** or **false**.   True   False

a)   Tyres have a tread so they grip onto the water in wet weather.   ☺   ☹

b)   The braking distance will be the same for all road surfaces.   ☺   ☹

c)   The more heavily a car is loaded, the shorter its stopping distance.   ☺   ☹

d)   The minimum legal tyre tread depth is 1.6 mm.   ☺   ☹

e)   The total stopping distance is the thinking distance + the braking distance.   ☺   ☹

Q4   Tyres should have a minimum tread depth to stop the car **aquaplaning** in wet conditions. What is "aquaplaning" and why is it **unsafe**?

....

....

Q5   A car is travelling along a dry country road at **90 km/h**. The driver sees a stop sign ahead of him and brakes. His thinking time is **0.6 s**.

You need to sort out the underlined units first for all of these questions.

a)   Work out his **thinking distance**.

....

b)   Once the driver hits the brakes the car decelerates at a constant rate and takes 3.8 s to come to a stop.

i)   Calculate the car's **average speed** (in m/s) during its deceleration.

....

ii)   Use your answer to part i) to help you calculate the car's **braking distance**.

....

Module P3 — Forces for Transport

Car Safety

Q1 A car travels along a level road and brakes to avoid hitting a cat.

a) What type of **energy** does the moving car have?

....

b) Explain how energy is **conserved** as the brakes slow down the car.

....

Q2 Use the words supplied to fill in the blanks in the passage below.

crashes	safety	power	interact	control

Many modern cars have active .... features. These ....

with the way the car is driven to help avoid .... These features

include ....-assisted steering and traction ....

Q3 The graph below shows the number of people killed in
motorway traffic accidents in the country of Thornland.

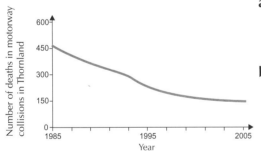

a) What is the overall trend shown by the graph?

....

b) Suggest a possible reason for this trend.

....

....

Q4 Modern cars are now fitted with many **safety features**.

a) Why are car safety features designed to **slow** the car
and its occupants down over the **longest** possible time in a collision?

....

....

b) State **two** safety features which increase the time taken for passengers to slow down in a crash.
For each feature, explain **how** it helps to convert kinetic energy more safely.

....

....

....

Car Safety

Q5   Since 1991 it has been compulsory in the UK for all adults
to wear seat belts in both the front and back seats of a car.

a)   Explain how a seat belt **absorbs** energy to slow down a passenger when a crash occurs.

....

b)   Why do seat belts have to be replaced after a crash? ....

....

Q6   A **safety cage** is a safety feature in a car.

a)   Is it a **passive** or an **active** safety feature? ....

b)   How does it keep the occupants safe?

....

....

Q7   Explain how **crash barriers** on roads can keep passengers safer in a collision.

....

....

Q8   Explain how the following features make driving a car safer.

a)   Adjustable seats.

....

b)   Control paddles near the steering wheel, e.g. stereo controls.

Control
Paddle

....

....

Q9   Two identical cars drive at the same speed down a dry road. One car is fitted with **ABS brakes**.
Both cars brake heavily at the same time. The car without ABS skids before coming to a halt.

a)   Are ABS brakes an **active** or a **passive** safety feature? ....

b)   Which car would you expect to have the shorter braking distance?
Explain your answer in terms of **friction**.

....

....

Work and Potential Energy

Q1   Jenny kicks a football, giving it **50 J** of energy.

  a) How much work does Jenny do?

....

  b) If Jenny kicks the ball with a force of **250 N**, over what **distance** does her kick act on the ball?

....

Q2   Explain why pushing your bicycle along a **level** road
means that you do some **work** in the scientific sense.

....

....

Q3   Indicate whether the following statements are **true** or **false**.

		True	False
a)	Potential energy = mass × g × height.	☐	☐
b)	Work done is the energy possessed by an object due to height.	☐	☐
c)	On Earth, the gravitational field strength is approximately **10 N/kg**.	☐	☐
d)	When a force moves an object, work is done.	☐	☐
e)	On Earth, a **3 kg** chicken flies up 2.5 m to sit on a fence. It gains about **75 J** of gravitational potential energy.	☐	☐

Q4   Dave works at a DIY shop. He has to load **28** flagstones onto the delivery truck.
Each flagstone has a mass of **25 kg** and has to be lifted **1.2 m** onto the truck.

  a) How much gravitational potential energy does one flagstone
gain when lifted onto the truck? (g = 10 N/kg)

....

  b) What is the **total gravitational potential energy** gained by the flagstones after they are all loaded
onto the truck?

....

  c) How much **work** does Dave do loading the truck?

....

....

Work and Potential Energy

Q5   Shelagh keeps fit by cycling every day. She's calculated that she applies a **steady force** of **50 N** as she cycles. She decides to do at least **80 kJ** of work at each session.

a)   What is the minimum distance Shelagh needs to cycle each session?

....

b)   Shelagh says "For every 80 kJ of work I do moving the bike, I must be using up exactly 80 kJ of energy from my food." Is she right? Explain your answer.

....

Q6   Jo is sitting at the top of a helter-skelter ride and her mass is **50 kg**.

g = 10 N/kg

a)   If her gravitational potential energy is **4000 J**, how high up is Jo?

....

b)   She comes down the helter-skelter and at the bottom her kinetic energy is **1500 J**. How much **energy** has been 'wasted' coming down the ride?

....

c)   Which **force** causes this energy to be wasted? ....

d)   If the ride is **50 m** long, what is the average energy-wasting force?

....

e)   Jo has another go on the helter-skelter but this time she slides down on a mat. At the bottom of the ride, her kinetic energy is **2000 J**. What is the average energy-wasting **force** on this turn on the ride?

....

....

f)   Explain why Jo has a **different** kinetic energy at the bottom when she slides down on a mat.

....

g)   At the bottom of the ride Jo and the mat take a distance of **5 m** to stop. What is the average stopping **force**?

....

....

|◄————————— 5 m —————————►|

Top Tips:
The main thing to remember is that **energy transferred** and **work done** are just the **same** thing.
You're bound to get asked to do a calculation, so make sure you know the couple of equations and
how to use them. All work questions are pretty similar — so just keep practising and you'll be fine.

Module P3 — Forces for Transport

Kinetic Energy

Q1 A car of mass **1000 kg** travels at **10 m/s**.

a) What is its **kinetic energy**?

....

b) Decide if the following statements are **true** or **false**.

	True	False
Kinetic energy is energy due to movement.	☺	☹
If a driver doubles her speed, her braking distance will be twice as far.	☺	☹
If the mass of a car is doubled, the braking distance will double.	☺	☹
Brakes convert kinetic energy into mostly heat energy to slow down a car.	☺	☹

Q2 A toy cricket ball hit straight upwards has a gravitational potential energy of **242 J** at the **top** of its flight.

a) What is the ball's **kinetic energy just** before it hits the ground?

....

b) Calculate the speed of the ball at this time if its mass is **100 g**.

....

Q3 A large truck and a car both have a kinetic energy of **614 400 J**. The mass of the truck is **12 288 kg** and the car **1200 kg**.

a) Calculate the **speed** of:

i) the car ....

ii) the truck ....

b) John is playing with his remote-controlled toy car and truck. The car's mass is 100 g. The truck's mass is 300 g. The car is moving twice as fast as the truck. Which has more kinetic energy — the car or the truck? Explain your answer.

....

Q4 Jack rides his bicycle along a level road and has a total kinetic energy of **1440 J**. He brakes, exerting a force of **200 N** on the wheels. How far does he travel before he stops?

....

> **Top Tips:** It's all about moving — the bigger the mass and the faster something moves the larger its kinetic energy. Get friendly with that formula — it crops up everywhere, especially in questions on energy conservation and work. It's not that bad really, so get learning.

Gravity and Roller Coasters

Q1 An astronaut goes to Mars to do some experiments.

Woohoo!
Who needs diets?
Just go to Mars...

a) Explain why her **mass** stays the same but her **weight** changes.

....

b) She takes a rock that weighs **50 N** on Earth. Using a set of scales designed
for use on Earth, she finds that the mass of the rock appears to be **1.9 kg** on Mars.
Calculate the **acceleration due to gravity** on Mars.

....

Q2 A roller coaster and passengers are stationary at the top of a ride.
At this point they have a gravitational potential energy of **300 kJ**.

a) Draw lines to connect the correct energy statement with each stage of the roller coaster.

A

B

C

D

minimum P.E., maximum K.E.

K.E. is being converted to P.E.

maximum P.E.

P.E. is being converted to K.E.

K.E. = Kinetic energy
P.E. = gravitational
potential energy

b) **i)** When the roller coaster is at half its original height, how much **kinetic energy** should it have?

....

ii) Explain why in real life the kinetic energy is **less** than this.

....

Q3 The planet Greldar has a large roller coaster.

a) If **g = 15 N/kg** on Greldar, calculate the **weight** of a full train if its mass is **1500 kg**.

....

b) At the start of the ride, the roller coaster rises up to its highest point of **25 m**.

i) What is its gain in gravitational **potential energy**?

....

ii) How much **work** does the motor need to do to get the roller coaster to the top of the ride?

....

Power

Q1 Complete this passage by using the words provided.

heat	energy	one hundred	rate	light	watts	joules

Power is the ………….. of doing work, or how much …………………. is

transferred per second. It is measured in …………………. or ………………………. per

second.

A 100 W light bulb transfers ……………………… joules of electrical energy into

………..……… and ……….…..…… each second.

Q2 George drives to work every day in a small car with a **power** output of **50 kW**.

a) Write down an equation that relates **power** to **energy**.

....

b) If the journey takes **5 minutes**, how much **energy** does the car get from its fuel?

....

c) One day George's car breaks down and so he cycles to work. The journey takes him
12 minutes and he uses **144 kJ** of energy. How much **power** does he generate?

....

Q3 Catherine and Sally decide to run up a set of stairs to see who can get to the
top more quickly. Catherine has a mass of **46 kg** and Sally has a mass of **48 kg**.

$g = 10 \text{ N/kg}$

a) The top of the stairs is **5 m** above ground.
Calculate the gain in **potential energy** for:

i) Catherine

....

46 kg

48 kg

5 m

ii) Sally

....

b) Catherine won the race in **6.2 s**, while Sally took **6.4 s**.
Which girl generated more **power**?

....

....

Power

Q4 Tom likes to build model boats. His favourite boat is the Carter, which has a motor power of **150 W**.

a) How much **energy** does the Carter transfer in **10 minutes**?

....

b) The petrol for the boat's motor can supply **30 kJ/ml**.
What volume of petrol is used up in **10 minutes**?

....

c) Tom decides to get a model speed boat which transfers **120 kJ** in the same 10 minute journey.
What is the **power** of the engine?

....

Q5 Josie runs home after school so she can watch her favourite TV programme.
She has a mass of **60 kg** and her school bag has a mass of **6 kg**.

a) At the start of her run, she accelerates steadily from **0** to **8 m/s** in **6 seconds** while carrying her bag.
Calculate her power for this part of her run.

....

b) Josie gets to her house, she puts **down** her school bag, and then runs up the stairs to her room.
It takes her **4 seconds** to get to the top of the stairs, where she is **5 m** above ground level.
How much power does she generate getting up the stairs?

....

Q6 Andy loves running and wants to improve his starts in sprint races. He uses a timing gate to
measure his maximum speed and how long the start takes him. He has a mass of **70 kg**.

Sprint number	Time taken (s)	Maximum speed (m/s)
1	3.2	8.0
2	3.1	8.2
3	3.3	7.9
4 *	4.6	7.2
5	3.2	7.9

*He slips at the start because his shoes don't grip properly.

a) Andy records data for five starts as shown.
Information for which start should be ignored?

....

b) Calculate the average **time** taken and the average **speed** achieved in the reliable starts.

....

....

c) What is Andy's average **power** over the reliable starts?

....

Module P3 — Forces for Transport

Fuels for Cars

Q1 Petrol is made from oil, which is a **fossil fuel**.

a) Are fossil fuels **renewable** or **non-renewable**? ....

b) Give **two** environmental problems that burning fossil fuels in cars can cause.

1. ....

2. ....

c) Give an example of an 'alternative fuel' to petrol and diesel. ....

Q2 Trevor's car has two engines, a normal **petrol engine** and an **electric motor**. He uses the electric motor for short journeys but uses the petrol engine for longer drives.

a) How does using the electric motor cause less damage to the **environment**?

....

b) Explain why Trevor has to use the petrol engine for **longer** journeys.

....

c) The electric motor is powered by batteries that need to be frequently charged from a mains supply. If Trevor always used the electric motor, would his driving have any impact on the environment? Explain your answer.

....

....

Q3 A car's fuel consumption is **3.4 l/100 km**. How much fuel is used in a **250 km** journey? Tick the correct box.

☐ 3.4 l ☐ 8.5 l ☐ 6.8 l ☐ 10.0 l

Q4 The fuel consumption of a car can **vary**.

a) State and explain why the following will **increase** or **decrease** the fuel consumption of a moving car.

i) Roof racks ....

....

ii) Open windows ....

....

b) How does fuel consumption vary with the **speed** of a car?

....

Mixed Questions — Module P3

Q1 Mr Alonso drives his car at a constant speed for **1500 m**. The engine produces a force of **300 N**.

300 N ➡

a) How much work does the engine do?

....

b) Mr Alonso then accelerates, increasing his speed by 20 m/s over 6.2 s. Calculate his acceleration.

....

c) As it's a hot day, Mr Alonso winds down his windows.
Explain how and why this will alter the **fuel consumption** of the car.

....

....

d) Explain how wearing a seat belt will keep Mr Alonso safer in a crash.

....

....

Q2 Jack and Jill go up a hill to go on a roller coaster. With them in it, the roller coaster carriage has a total mass of **1200 kg**.

a) What is the weight of the carriage? (Assume $g = 10$ m/s^2.) ....

b) At the start of the ride the carriage rises up to its highest point of **34 m** above the ground and stops. Calculate its gain in potential energy.

....

c) The carriage then falls to a third of its maximum height. Assuming there is no air resistance or friction, calculate the speed of the carriage at this point.

....

....

....

d) At the end of the ride, the carriage slows down, decelerating at **6.4 m/s^2**.
How long does it take the carriage to slow down from 20 m/s and come to a stop?

....

....

Module P3 — Forces for Transport

Mixed Questions — Module P3

Q3 Norman loves trainspotting. As a special treat, he not only notes the train numbers but plots a **distance-time** graph for two of the trains.

a) For how long is train 2 stationary?

....

b) Both trains start at a steady speed. How do we know this?

....

c) Calculate the initial speed of the faster train.

....

d) Describe the motion of train 1 between 40 s and 80 s.

....

Q4 Cherie robs a bank and escapes in a getaway car with a mass of **2100 kg**. She travels at a constant speed of **90 km/h** along a straight, level road.

a) Calculate the kinetic energy of the car.

....

b) Is there a resultant force on the car? Explain your answer.

....

c) A police car swings into the middle of the road and stops ahead of Cherie's car. Cherie brakes with a reaction time of **0.7 s** and a braking time of **3.2 s**.

   i) Calculate her thinking distance.

   ....

   ii) What happens to the kinetic energy of the car as Cherie slows down?

   ....

d) The getaway car has ABS brakes.

   i) Are ABS brakes an active or passive safety feature? ....

   ii) How would you expect having ABS brakes to influence Cherie's braking distance?

   ....

74

Mixed Questions — Module P3

Q5 In the film 'Crouching Sparrow, Hidden Beaver', a **95 kg** dummy is dropped **60 m** from the top of a building. (Assume that g = 10 m/s².)

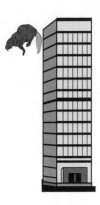

a) Sketch a distance-time graph and a velocity-time graph for the dummy from the moment it is dropped until just after it hits the ground. (Ignore air resistance and assume the dummy does not reach a terminal speed.)

b) Do any forces act on the dummy when it lies still on the ground (after falling)? If so, what are they?

....

c) The take doesn't go to plan so the dummy is lifted back to the top of the building using a motor.

i) How much work is done on the dummy to get it to the top of the building?

....

ii) The useful power output of the motor is **760 W**. How long does it take to get the dummy to the top of the building?

....

Q6 A sky-diver jumps out of an aeroplane. Her weight is **700 N**.

a) What force causes her to accelerate downwards?

....

b) After **10 s** she is falling at a steady speed of **60 m/s**. State the force of air resistance that is acting on her.

....

c) She now opens her parachute, which increases the air resistance to **2000 N**. Explain what happens immediately after she opens the parachute.

....

....

d) After falling with her parachute open for **5 s**, the sky-diver is travelling at a steady speed of **4 m/s**. What is the air resistance force now?

....

Module P3 — Forces for Transport

Static Electricity

Q1   **Circle** the pairs of charges that would attract each other and **underline** those that would repel.

positive and positive   positive and negative   negative and positive   negative and negative

Q2   Fill in the gaps in these sentences with the words below.

electrons	positive	static	friction	insulating	negative

.... electricity can build up when two .... materials are rubbed together. The .... moves .... from one material onto the other. This leaves a .... charge on one of the materials and a .... charge on the other.

Q3   The sentences below are wrong. Write out a **correct** version for each.

a)   A polythene rod becomes negatively charged when rubbed with a duster because it loses electrons.

....

....

b)   A charged polythene rod will repel small pieces of paper if they are placed near it.

....

....

c)   The closer two charged objects are together, the less strongly they attract or repel.

....

....

d)   If a positively charged object is connected to earth by a metal strap, electrons flow through the strap from the object to the ground, and the object is safely discharged.

....

....

e)   Build-up of static can cause sparks if the distance between the object and the earth is big enough.

....

....

Static Electricity

Q4 A library had to be closed after nylon carpets were fitted. People complained of electric shocks when they touched the metal handrail on the stairs. Explain why they were experiencing shocks.

....

....

Q5 Russell hates his blue jumper. Whenever he takes it off his hair stands on end. Explain why this happens.

....

....

Q6 Choose from the words below to complete the passage.

fuel   explosion   metal   paper rollers   wood   grain chutes   sparks   earthing   plastic

Static electricity can be dangerous when refuelling cars. If too much static builds up, there

might be .... which could set fire to the ....

This could lead to an .... To prevent this happening, the nozzle is

made of .... so the charge is conducted away. There are similar safety

problems with .... and ....

Q7 As Peter switched off his TV, he noticed that the screen was dusty. When he wiped it with his finger he heard a **crackling** sound and felt a slight **electric shock**.

Peter made two statements about what happened. Give a **reason** why he said each of the following:

a) "*The screen must have been at a high voltage.*"

....

....

b) "*When I touched it, part of the screen was discharged to earth.*"

....

....

Q8 Explain why **anti-static** sprays are sometimes used in hospital operating theatres.

....

....

Uses of Static Electricity

Q1   The diagram shows an electrostatic paint sprayer.

a)   How do the drops of paint become charged?

....

b)   Why does this help produce a fine spray?

....

c)   Explain how the paint drops are attracted to the object being sprayed.

....

d)   Explain why the object being painted doesn't need to be turned round while it is being sprayed.

....

Q2   Complete this paragraph by choosing words from the list below.

precipitator	negative	plates	charge	particles	positive	heavy
	attracted	fall off	electron	compressed		

Smoke contains tiny .... The smoke can be cleaned up with a dust

....

One sort uses a wire grid with a high negative .... to give the particles a

negative charge. They then pass between two metal .... which have

a .... charge.

The particles are .... to the plates. The particles clump together

and when they are .... enough, they ....

Q3   A defibrillator is a machine used by emergency medical staff to give electric shocks.

a)   When are defibrillators used and why?

....

b)   How is the electricity transferred to the patient?

....

c)   Explain what safety precautions are taken when using a defibrillator and why.

....

....

Charge in Circuits

Q1   Use the words below to complete the passage.
You may need to use some words more than once.

protons	electrons	resistance	voltage	increase	reduce

Current is the flow of .... around a circuit. Current flows through a

component which has a .... across it. Resistance tends to

.... the flow. To increase the current in a circuit you can

.... the resistance or .... the voltage.

Q2   Connect the quantities
with their units.

A   Current   volts

V   Resistance   amps

Ω   Voltage   ohms

Q3   The flow of electricity in circuits can be compared to the flow of water in pipes.

a)   In a water 'circuit', what is the equivalent to electrical **current**?

    ....

Low Pressure   **Pump**   High Pressure

Flow of water

Constriction

b)   If there is a water pump in the system,
what electrical device does it correspond to?

    ....

c)   What corresponds to electrical **resistance** in a water 'circuit'?

    ....

d)   The pump is turned up. What would the equivalent action be in an electrical circuit?

    ....

Q4   A current flows around an electrical circuit.

a)   If the circuit is broken, what happens to the current?

    ....

b)   Give an example of a safety feature designed to break a circuit.

    ....

Top Tips: The current is the flow of electrons which are pushed around a circuit by the
voltage. The greater the voltage, the more current flows. Anything that slows the flow of electrons
down is a resistor. Slowing the electrons decreases the current. Make sure you get the hang of this
and you'll be scooping up the marks like a small child let loose at the pick and mix counter. Enjoy.

Fuses and Safe Plugs

Q1   Answer the following questions about **electric plugs**:

  a) Why is the body of a plug made of rubber or plastic?

    ....

  b) Explain why some parts of a plug are made from copper or brass.

    ....

  c) What material is the cable insulation made from, and why?

    ....

Q2   Use the words below to complete these rules for wiring a plug.

        outer   bare   live   earth   neutral   insulation   firmly   green and yellow

  a) Strip the .... off the end of each wire.

  b) Connect the brown wire to the .... terminal.

  c) Connect the blue wire to the .... terminal.

  d) Connect the .... wire to the .... terminal.

  e) Check all the wires are .... screwed in with no .... bits showing.

  f) The cable grip must be securely fastened over the .... covering of the cable.

Q3   This plug is **incorrectly** wired. Write down the **three** mistakes.

  1. ....

  2. ....

  3. ....

    = Neutral
    = Live
    = Earth

Q4   Put these events in the correct order to describe what happens
when a fault occurs in an earthed kettle. Label the events from 1 to 4.

  ☐ **The device is isolated from the live wire.**   ☐ **A big current flows out through the earth wire.**

  ☐ **A big surge in current blows the fuse.**   ☐ **A fault allows the live wire to touch the metal case.**

Q5   A '**double insulated**' hairdryer uses a current of 0.25 A.

  a) Andrea has fuses rated 0.25 A, 2 A and 8 A.
Which fuse should she fit in the plug for the hairdryer? ....

  b) Why does the hairdryer **not** need an **earth wire**?

    ....

Resistance

Q1 Indicate whether these statements are **true** or **false**.

	True	False
Current flows from positive to negative.	☐	☐
An ammeter should be connected in parallel with a component.	☐	☐
Items that are in series can be in any order.	☐	☐
A voltmeter should be connected in series with a component.	☐	☐

Q2 Complete these sentences by circling the correct word from each pair.

a) Increasing the voltage increases / decreases the current that flows.

b) If the p.d. is kept constant, to increase the current you need to increase / decrease the resistance.

c) If the resistance is increased, more / less current will flow if the p.d. is kept constant.

Q3 Fabio sets up a standard circuit using a **variable resistor** to test the resistance of a material.

a) Label the standard test circuit components using the words in the box below.

> voltmeter   material
> variable resistor   ammeter

b) Fabio sets the variable resistor at zero resistance. He measures a current of 2.4 A and a p.d. of 6 V. Calculate the resistance of the material.

....

c) How would Fabio use the variable resistor to help get a reliable result from his experiment?

....

Q4 Fill in the missing values in the table below.

Ir-resistor-ble.

Voltage (V)	Current (A)	Resistance (Ω)
6	2	
8		2
	3	3
4	8	
2		4
	0.5	2

Ultrasound Scans and Treatment

Q1   Sound waves are **longitudinal** waves.

a)   Describe the difference between **longitudinal** and **transverse** waves.

....

....

b)   What is meant by the **frequency** of a wave?

....

c)   When sound waves travel through a material they produce **compressions** and **rarefactions**. What do these words mean?

....

....

Q2   An oscilloscope (CRO) can be used to show a sound wave as a **transverse** wave.

a)   Mark the **wavelength** and the **amplitude** of the wave on the diagram.

b)   i)   What does the **amplitude** of a wave tell you?

....

....

ii)   If a sound wave has a small amplitude, will it sound loud or quiet? ....

Q3   A concentrated beam of **ultrasound** can be used to treat kidney stones.

a)   What is ultrasound?

....

b)   What effect does the ultrasound beam have on kidney stones?

....

c)   How are the kidney stone remains removed from the body?

....

d)   Give two reasons why using ultrasound is a good way of treating kidney stones.

1.   ....

2.   ....

Ultrasound Scans and Treatment

Q4   Ultrasound can be used to monitor the growth of a foetus.

a)   Complete the following using words from the list.

foetus   reflected   media   detected   echoes   body   image

Ultrasound waves can pass through most parts of the ....

Whenever an ultrasound wave reaches the boundary between two different

.............................., some of the wave is .... back and can be

.... These .... can be processed by a computer

to give an .... of the ....

b)   Give one other use of ultrasound in medicine, apart from
prenatal scanning and kidney stone treatment.

....

Q5   Indicate whether the following statements are **true** or **false**.

	True	False
Ultrasound waves have frequencies greater than 20 000 Hz.	☐	☐
X-rays are used for prenatal scanning.	☐	☐
Ultrasound can cause cancer if a patient is exposed to a high dose.	☐	☐
X-rays travel easily through soft tissue.	☐	☐
Ultrasound and X-rays are both good ways of looking at broken bones in the body.	☐	☐

Q6   Ultrasound can be used in a similar way to **X-rays**.

a)   Why is ultrasound safer than X-rays?

....

b)   State whether X-rays or ultrasound would be used to
investigate a suspected broken bone, and explain why.

....

....

Top Tips: Amazing really that you can learn so much using sound waves. The main thing
to remember is that ultrasound is safe and extremely useful. You might be asked to explain **how**
ultrasound is used in prenatal scans and for removing kidney stones — so make sure you know.

Ionising Radiation

Q1 X-rays and gamma rays are electromagnetic waves.

a) Describe how gamma rays are released.

....

b) How are X-rays produced?

....

c) Which of the two is easier to control? Explain your answer.

....

Q2 Use the words in the list below to complete the paragraph.

ionisation	nuclear	molecules	cells	cancer	destroy

When X-ray and .... radiation enter .... in the body
they may collide with .... and cause .... Fairly low
doses of radiation can cause .... — creating mutant cells which
multiply uncontrollably. Higher doses can .... cells completely.

Q3 The three different types of nuclear radiation can all be dangerous.

a) Which **two** types of radiation can pass into the human body
from outside? Circle the correct answers.

alpha   beta   gamma

b) **i)** Which type of radiation is usually most dangerous if it's inhaled or swallowed? ....

ii) Describe the effects this type of radiation can have on the human body.

....

....

Q4 When radiographers take X-ray 'photographs' or scans of patients, they themselves are exposed to
X-rays. Write down two precautions radiographers can take to minimise their exposure to X-rays.

1. ....

2. ....

Radioactive Decay

Q1   Write down the atomic number and mass number for each type of radiation.

a)   alpha   atomic number = ...   mass number = ...

b)   beta   atomic number = ...   mass number = ...

c)   gamma   atomic number = ...   mass number = ...

Q2   Complete the passage using words from the list.

chemical random decay radiation nucleus element temperature

Radioactive .... is a totally .... process.

At some point an unstable .... will decay and emit

.... What is left behind is often a new ....

There is nothing that can make an unstable nucleus decay. It is unaffected by

.... or .... bonding.

Q3   Complete the table below by choosing the correct word from each column.

Radiation Type	Ionising power weak/moderate/ strong	Charge positive/none/ negative	Relative mass no mass/ small/large	Penetrating power low/moderate/ high	Relative speed slow/fast/ very fast
alpha					
beta					
gamma					

Q4   When a nucleus emits an alpha or beta particle, the nucleus changes.

a)   What happens to a nucleus when it emits an **alpha particle**?

....

....

....

b)   What happens to a nucleus when it emits a **beta particle**?

....

....

Radioactive Decay

Q5 Explain clearly why:

a) an alpha particle is written as $^4_2$He or $^4_2\alpha$.

....

b) a radium atom $^{226}_{88}$Ra turns into a radon atom $^{222}_{86}$Rn when it emits an alpha particle.

....

c) a beta particle is written as $^0_{-1}$e or $^0_{-1}\beta$.

....

d) a carbon-14 atom $^{14}_6$C turns into a nitrogen atom $^{14}_7$N when it emits a beta particle.

....

Q6 The diagram shows uranium-238 decaying into thorium by alpha and gamma emission.

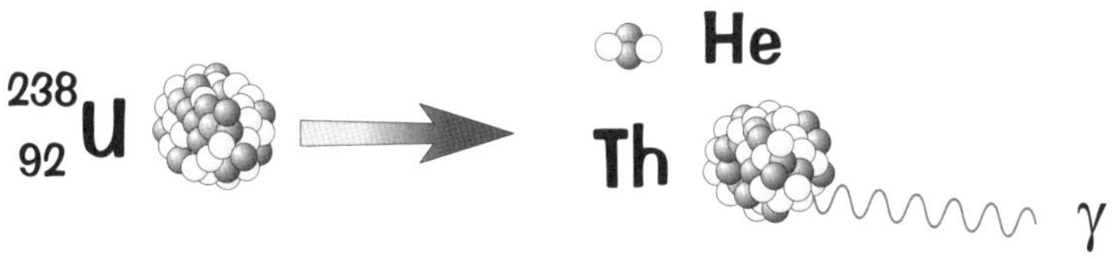

$$^{238}_{92}U \longrightarrow Th \quad He \quad \gamma$$

a) What effect does the **gamma ray** emission have on the uranium nucleus?

....

b) Write the full nuclear equation for this decay, clearly showing the atomic and mass numbers.

....

Q7 When radioactive decay occurs, α, β or γ radiation is emitted and new elements may be formed.

a) Write a nuclear equation to show thorium-234, $^{234}_{90}$Th, decaying to form protactinium, $^{234}_{91}$Pa .

....

b) Write a nuclear equation to show radon, $^{222}_{86}$Rn , decaying by **alpha** emission.

....

Top Tips: Put 'nuclear' in front of anything and it sounds extra scary*. Fortunately, nuclear **equations** aren't nearly as scary as they sound. Learn the atomic numbers and mass numbers for each type of radiation and you'll be well on the way to equation bliss. After a bit of practice you'll find that balancing the equations isn't that bad — just a bit of adding and subtracting. *except the word **sheep**

Radioactivity and Half-Life

Q1   Complete the passage using some of the words given below.

| long photo time all half ionise atoms gamma alpha |
| beta short increases decreases decay |

The radioactivity of a sample always .... over time. Each time a decay

happens ...., ... or .... radiation is emitted.

The half-life is the .... taken for .... of the unstable

.... now present to .... An isotope with a ....

half-life decays more quickly than an isotope with a .... half-life.

Q2   The graph shows how the count rate of a radioactive isotope declines with time.

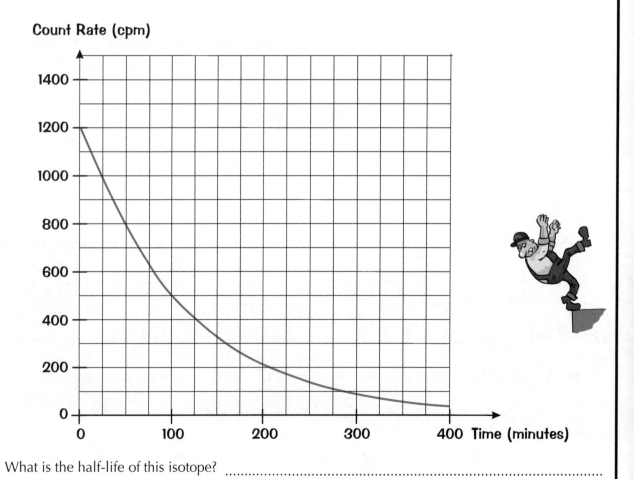

Count Rate (cpm)

a)   What is the half-life of this isotope? ....

b)   What was the count rate after 3 half-lives? ....

c)   What fraction of the original radioactive nuclei will still be unstable after 5 half-lives?

....

d)   After how long was the count rate down to 100? ....

Radioactivity and Half-Life

Q3 The activity of a radioisotope is 960 cpm. 1 hour later, the activity has dropped to 15 cpm. What is the source's half-life? Tick the correct box.

☐ 15 mins   ☐ 10 mins   ☐ 12 mins   ☐ 3 mins

Q4 The half-life of uranium-238 is 4500 million years. The half-life of carbon-14 is 5730 years.

a) What do the '238' in "uranium-238" and the '14' in "carbon-14" mean?

....

....

b) If you start with a sample of each element and the two samples have equal activity, which will lose its radioactivity more quickly? Circle the correct answer.

uranium-238   carbon-14

You'll need to change 6 minutes into seconds.

Q5 A radioactive isotope has a half-life of 40 seconds.

a) What fraction of the original unstable nuclei will still be present after 6 minutes?

....

....

b) i) If the initial count rate of the sample was 8000 counts per minute, what would be the approximate count rate after 6 minutes?

....

....

ii) After how many whole **minutes** would the count rate have fallen below 10 counts per minute?

....

....

Q6 Nick was trying to explain half-life to his little brother. He said, "isotopes with a long half-life are always more dangerous than those with a short half-life."

Is Nick right? Explain your answer.

....

....

....

88

Background Radiation

Q1 Which of the following are **true?** Circle the appropriate letters.

A About half of the UK's background radiation comes from radon gas.

B The nuclear industry is responsible for about 10% of background radiation in the UK.

C If there were no radioactive substances on Earth, there would be no background radiation.

Q2 The level of background radiation varies from place to place. For each of the following, indicate whether the background level will be **higher** or **lower** than average and explain your answer.

a) In a plane at high altitude, the level will be **higher / lower** than average because:

....

b) In a mine, the level will usually be **higher / lower** than average because:

....

c) In houses built above granite rocks, the level will usually be **higher / lower** than average because:

....

Q3 Peter did an experiment to compare equal quantities of two radioactive materials. Here are his results and conclusion.

Material tested	Radiation measured (counts per second)
None	50
Material A	200
Material B	400

CONCLUSION
"Both materials are radioactive. Material B is twice as radioactive as Material A."

Is Peter's conclusion correct? Give a reason for your answer.

....

....

Q4 The concentration of **radon** gas found in people's homes varies across the UK.

a) Why does the concentration vary across the country?

....

b) Explain why high concentrations of radon are dangerous.

....

c) How can people in high radon areas reduce the radon concentration in their homes?

....

Medical Uses of Radiation

Q1 Complete the following paragraph on radiotherapy using the words provided.

| ill   centre   normal   kill   cells   focused   cancer   rotating   radiotherapy |

High doses of gamma radiation will .... living ....

Because of this, gamma radiation is used to treat .... This is called

....

Gamma rays are .... on the tumour using a wide beam. Damage to

.... cells can make the patient feel very .... This damage

is minimised by .... the radioactive source around the body, keeping the

tumour at the ....

Q2 Iodine-131 is commonly used as a tracer in medicine.

a) Normal iodine has a mass number of 127. Why is it no good as a tracer?

....

b) The thyroid gland normally absorbs iodine.
Describe how iodine-131 can be used to detect if the thyroid gland is working properly.

....

....

....

....

Q3 The table shows the properties of four radioisotopes.

a) Which radioisotope would be best to use as a medical tracer and why?

....

....

....

Radioisotope	Half-life	Type of emission
technetium-99	6 hours	beta/gamma
phosphorus-32	14 days	beta
cobalt-60	5 years	beta/gamma

b) Which radioisotope would a hospital use to treat cancer patients? Explain your answer.

....

....

Medical Uses of Radiation

Q4 The diagram shows how radiation can be used to sterilise surgical instruments.

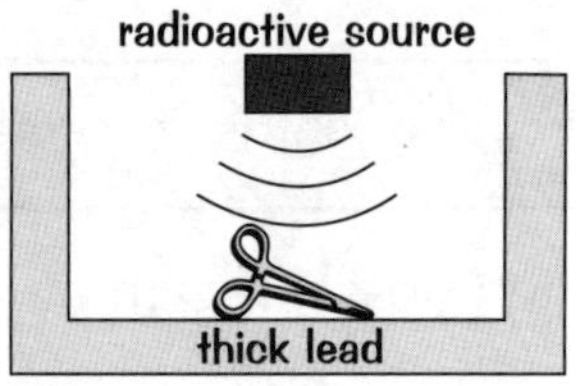

radioactive source

thick lead

a) What kind of radioactive source is used, and why? In your answer, mention the **type** of radiation emitted (α, β or γ) and the **half-life** of the source.

....

....

....

b) What is the purpose of the thick lead?

....

c) Similar machines can be used to treat fruit before it is exported from South America to Europe, to stop it going bad on the long journey. How does irradiating the fruit help?

....

....

Q5 A patient has a radioactive source injected into her body to test her kidneys.

A healthy kidney will get rid of the radioactive material quickly (to the bladder). Damaged kidneys take longer to do this.

The results of the test, for both the patient's kidneys, are shown opposite.

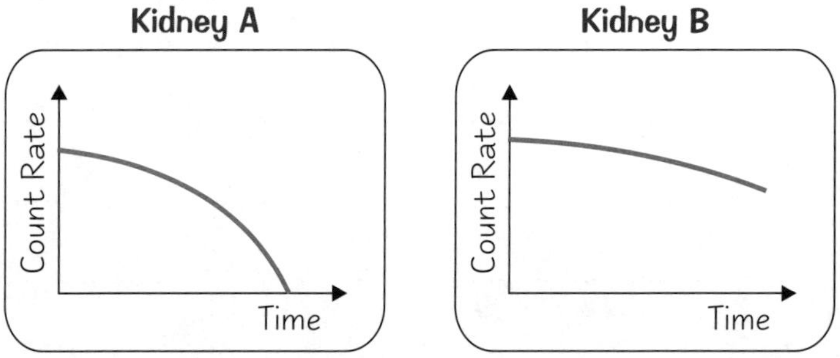

Kidney A

Count Rate

Time

Kidney B

Count Rate

Time

a) Explain how the doctor knew which kidney was working well and which was not.

....

....

b) Explain why an alpha source would **not** be suitable for this investigation.

....

....

Top Tips: There's no doubt about it — this is physics being obviously, genuinely **useful** — and radiation being Mr Nice Guy. Anyway, make sure you know **why** each type of radiation is used in each situation — and remember that you **never** want an alpha source inside the body. Final tip: saying "radioisotope" three times every day for a year can increase your IQ by 20 points.

Non-Medical Uses of Radiation

Q1   The table shows some commonly used radioisotopes and the type of radiation they emit.

a)   Which of these isotopes would be most
suitable for these applications?

   i)   A smoke detector

....

   ii)   To sterilise pre-packed food

....

Radioisotope	Decays by...
strontium-90	beta emission
americium-241	mainly alpha emission
cobalt-60	beta and gamma emission

   iii)   To measure the thickness of paper as it is being manufactured

....

b)   What further information about these isotopes would you want before you considered using them?

....

Q2   Carbon-14 makes up 1/10 000 000 of the carbon in the air.

a)   Name one gas in the air which contains carbon.

....

b)   What proportion of the carbon present in organisms alive now is carbon-14?

....

c)   What happens to the level of carbon-14 in a plant or animal after it dies?

....

Q3   The following sentences explain how a smoke detector works, but they are in the wrong order.

Put them in order by labelling them 1 (first) to 6 (last).

☐ The circuit is broken so no current flows.

1 The radioactive source emits alpha particles.

☐ A current flows between the electrodes — the alarm stays off.

☐ The alarm sounds.

☐ The air between the electrodes is ionised by the alpha particles.

☐ A fire starts and smoke particles absorb the alpha radiation.

?

Non-Medical Uses of Radiation

Q4 Eviloilco knows that its oil pipeline is leaking somewhere between points A and B.

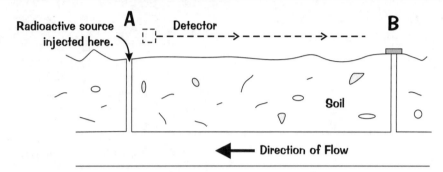

Radioactive source injected here. **A** Detector **B**

Soil

← Direction of Flow

This is how Eviloilco plans to find the leak.

> We will inject a source of alpha radiation into the pipeline at point A. (This source has a long half-life — giving us better value for money in the long term.) After injecting the radioactive material, we will pass a sensor along the surface above the pipeline — and so detect where radiation is escaping, hence pinpointing the leak.

a) Give **two** reasons why Eviloilco has made a bad choice of radioactive source, and describe the type of source they should use.

....

....

....

b) Even if they use the correct type of radioactive source, their plan will still fail. Why?

....

Q5 A wooden spoon from an archaeological dig was found to have 1 part C-14 to 80 000 000 parts carbon. Work out when the wood was **living material**. (The half-life of C-14 is 5730 years.)

....

Q6 Uranium-238 has a half-life of 4.5 billion years.

a) Explain how the decay of uranium can be used to date rocks.

Rock, 243 019 yrs, but young at heart. Cumbria based, GSOH. Likes: the outdoors. Dislikes: dogs, moss

Mal 45, seek cur foot mor

....

....

b) The Earth is around 4.5 billion years old. How much of the Earth's original uranium-238 is left?

....

c) A meteorite contains uranium-238 and lead in a ratio of 1:3. How old is the meteorite?

....

Nuclear Power

Q1 Choose from the following words to complete the passage.

split	chemical	turbine	electricity	uranium	water	wine
	steam	moped	generator	reactors	heat	

Inside a nuclear reactor, ... or plutonium atoms

.... and release .... energy. This

energy is used to turn .... into ....

The steam then turns a ...., which in turn drives a

.............................., producing ....

Q2 In a nuclear reactor a controlled fission **chain reaction** takes place.

a) Describe a fission **chain reaction**, starting with a single uranium nucleus absorbing a **slow-moving neutron**.

....

....

....

....

b) Write a nuclear equation for an atom of uranium-235 absorbing a neutron.

....

Q3 Nuclear reactors have **control rods**, which are usually made of boron.

a) How do these boron rods control the reaction?

....

b) What would happen if there were **no** control rods (or other control mechanism) in the reactor?

....

c) What would happen if there were **too many** control rods in the reactor?

....

Nuclear Power

Q4   The diagram shows a gas-cooled nuclear reactor.

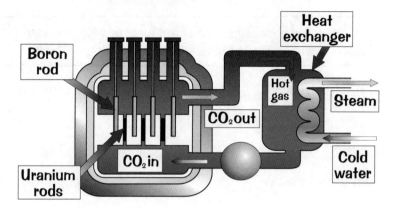

a)   Why do there have to be free neutrons in the reactor to start it up?

....

b)   Describe how heat is generated in the reactor.

....

....

c)   What is the function of the carbon dioxide?

....

d)   Why is the reactor surrounded with a very thick layer of concrete?

....

Q5   Uranium-236 is an unstable isotope of uranium.

a)   Describe how uranium-236 is formed inside a nuclear reactor.

....

b)   U-236 decays to form two neutrons and two new elements: krypton-90 and barium-144.
        Write the nuclear equation for this decay. (Atomic masses Kr = 36, Ba = 56, U = 92.)

....

Top Tips: The key thing with nuclear power is to remember what goes on in the reactor.
It's really just one big nuclear kettle. A controlled chain reaction is set up and releases heat, which is
used to heat water and produce steam. After that it's just like almost all power stations — the steam
turns a turbine which turns a generator which makes electricity, which makes cups of tea galore.

Mixed Questions — Module P4

Q1   The diagram shows an aircraft being refuelled. No safety precautions have been taken.

a)   i)   Explain how static electricity could cause an explosion in this situation.

....

....

   ii)   Give one precaution that can be taken to avoid this danger.

....

b)   The aircraft needs a new lick of paint. Describe how static electricity could be used
to make sure that an even coat of paint is sprayed onto the aircraft.

....

....

Q2   Radioactive tracers are important in medicine and industry.

a)   Explain what is meant by the word 'tracer'.

....

b)   Give two reasons why an alpha source would not be suitable to use as a **medical** tracer.

....

....

c)   Give one example of how tracers are used in industry.

....

Q3   The diagram below shows part of a chain reaction.

a)   What is the name of the type of radioactive decay shown in the diagram?   ....

b)   This decay happens as part of a chain reaction. Describe what happens in this chain reaction.

....

....

Mixed Questions — Module P4

Q4 Approximately one in 10 000 000 of the carbon molecules found in living plants or animals are atoms of the radioactive isotope carbon-14. After a plant or animal dies this proportion starts to decrease. Carbon-14 has a half-life of 5730 years.

a) Calculate the fraction of the atoms in a pure sample of carbon-14 that will still not have decayed after 10 half-lives have gone by.

....

....

b) Approximately how old is a bone fragment in which the proportion of carbon-14 is one part in 50 000 000? Explain your answer.

....

....

....

c) Suggest why carbon dating is unreliable for samples more than about 50 000 years old.

....

....

Q5 Paul wants to set the mood for his date with some romantic lighting. He dims the lights using a dimmer switch which works as a variable resistor.

a) Describe how the dimmer switch dims the lights.

....

....

Position	Resistance	Current
1	50	
2		2.3
3		9.2

b) Because he's such a charmer, Paul entertains his date by taking some current and resistance readings with the dimmer switch in three different positions. The voltage is 230 V. Complete the table.

c) In which position will the lights be brightest? ....

Q6 Ultra sound and X-rays are both used in medicine.

a) Explain how ultrasound is used in prenatal scans.

....

....

b) Why would you not use X-rays for this type of scan?

....

Mixed Questions — Module P4

Q7 Modern electrical appliances are carefully designed to prevent the user getting an electric shock.

a) Tom's washing machine develops a fault. Part of the live wire touches the metal case.
Explain how the earth wire and fuse work together to prevent Tom getting an electric shock.

....

....

b) Bob buys a new 'double insulated' television set.

i) Which wires are in the plug? ....

ii) What is meant by 'double insulated'?

....

Q8 Fay measures the count rate of a sample of pure copper-64 in her home,
using a Geiger counter. The graph below shows her results.

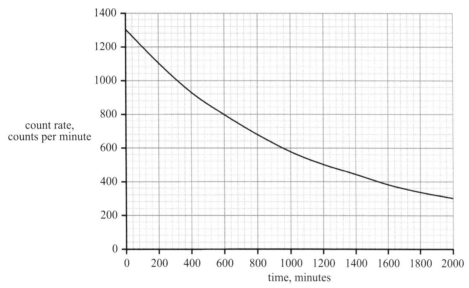

a) Fay had previously measured the background rate to be 100 counts per minute.
Find the half-life of copper-64.

....

b) She takes her Geiger counter to her friend's house and finds the background rate is much higher.
Give one reason why background radiation changes from place to place?

....

c) Her friend explains that she lives in a high **radon** area.

i) What disease is her friend more at risk of developing? ....

ii) How could she reduce the concentration of radon in her house?

....

Satellites

Q1 Some satellites have **geosynchronous orbits**. Others have **polar** orbits.

a) i) Complete the following by circling the correct words.

A geosynchronous satellite is in a low / high orbit over the Earth's equator / poles.

ii) Explain how polar-orbiting satellites can scan the whole of the Earth's surface every day.

....

....

b) On the diagram, draw the orbits of a polar satellite and a geosynchronous satellite.

Label the polar orbit '**P**' and the geosynchronous orbit '**G**'.

Q2 Answer the following questions on **geosynchronous** and **polar** orbits.

a) Why is it useful for a **communications** satellite to be in a **geosynchronous** orbit?

....

b) If you lived on the **equator**, which way would you point a satellite dish so that you could pick up a signal from a **communications** satellite?

....

c) How long does a **geosynchronous** satellite take to make **one** complete orbit of the Earth?

....

d) There is enough space to put many more than 400 satellites in a geosynchronous orbit. In practice, why wouldn't we be able to use more than about 400 geostationary satellites?

....

e) What is the main **advantage** of a polar orbit?

....

f) Explain why the polar orbits of spy satellites need to be **low**.

....

....

g) Apart from spying, state one other common use for a satellite in low polar orbit. ....

Gravity and Orbits

Q1 Indicate whether the following statements about gravity are **true** or **false**.

True False

a) Gravity can attract and repel other masses. ☐ ☐

b) Gravity is a weak force and is only noticeable if one of the masses is really big. ☐ ☐

c) Earth's gravity gets weaker the higher up you go. ☐ ☐

d) All other things being equal, heavy things accelerate to the ground more quickly than lighter things. ☐ ☐

e) The Sun's gravity makes the Earth orbit around it. ☐ ☐

f) The Sun's gravity makes the Moon orbit the Earth. ☐ ☐

Q2 This is a diagram of a **planet** orbiting the Sun.

a) Draw an arrow on the diagram to show the direction of the Sun's **gravitational force** on the planet and label it 'F'.

b) Now draw an arrow showing the direction of the planet's **velocity** and label it 'V'.

c) i) What is the special name given to a force that makes an object move in a circle?

....

ii) In what direction does this force always act?

....

Q3 Here is a diagram of a **comet**'s orbit around the Sun. **A**, **B**, **C** and **D** are different points on the orbit.

a) Answer each of the following questions with the correct letter A-D.

i) At which point on the orbit is the comet travelling the slowest? ....

ii) At which point on the orbit is the comet travelling the quickest? ....

b) Explain why the speed of the comet changes in different parts of its orbit.

....

....

Gravity and Orbits

Q4 The table below contains data about the orbits of six of the planets which orbit the Sun.

A.U. = astronomical unit — the distance from the Earth to the Sun.

	Mercury	Venus	Earth	Mars	Jupiter	Saturn
Distance from Sun (A.U)	0.39	0.72	1.00	1.52	5.20	9.54
Time for one orbit (Earth years)	0.24	0.62	1.00	1.88	11.9	29.5

a) What can you conclude from the data? Circle the letters of any of the following which apply.

   A The further out the planet is from the Sun, the weaker the Sun's gravity.

   B The time it takes a planet to orbit the Sun is directly proportional to its distance from the Sun.

   C The further out the planet is from the Sun, the longer it takes to orbit.

   D Planets further out than Saturn will take longer than 29.5 years to orbit the Sun.

b) Why are the orbits of geostationary satellites higher up than those of polar satellites?

   ....

   ....

Q5 The force of gravity depends on the distance between masses.

a) If you double the distance you are from a planet, what happens to the force of its gravity on you?

   ....

b) A satellite orbiting the Earth feels a gravitational force of **250 N**.
   What gravitational force would the same satellite feel if its orbit were moved to be:

   i) five times further away from the Earth?

   ....

   ....

   ....

   ii) half the distance from the Earth?

   ....

   ....

   ....

Top Tips: Watch out with that old inverse square law*. Don't forget the "square" bit, or the "inverse" bit — it's easy to rush things and end up making a mistake. It's the inverse square law that explains why comets move the way they do, in those long orbits. *It <u>doesn't</u> mean "always give your answer as a poem."

Module P5 — Space for Reflection

Speed and Velocity

Q1 Write down whether each of the following statements applies to **speed** only, **velocity** only or **both**.

a) It changes if the **direction** changes. ....

b) It is a **scalar**. ....

c) Its units could be **km/h**. ....

d) It is a **vector**. ....

e) If I **accelerate** then this quantity **must** change. ....

f) If I **accelerate** this quantity **might not** change. ....

Look back at Module P3 if you're not sure about these ones.

Q2 Fill in the boxes with **words** or with the **symbols** +, −, × or ÷ to complete these formulas.

a) Average speed ☐ distance ☐ time

b) Distance ☐ average speed ☐ time

c) Time = ☐ ÷ average speed

Q3 Use your answers to Q2 to help you answer the following.

a) A bus travelled 24 km in 40 minutes.

　i) What was the average speed of the bus, in **m/s**?

　..

　..

　ii) At this speed, how far would the bus travel in one and a half hours?

　..

b) Answering an emergency call, PC Kent drives his police car at **200 km/h**.
At this speed, how long would it take PC Kent to reach the emergency which is **8 km** away?

....

c) A taxi travels for 10 km at a speed of 40 km/h and then 40 km at a speed of 100 km/h.
What is the average speed for the whole journey?

....

....

....

Speed and Velocity

Q4 Susan walked from her house to the newsagent's.
She bought a magazine and then walked back home.
Here is a **distance/time graph** of her journey:

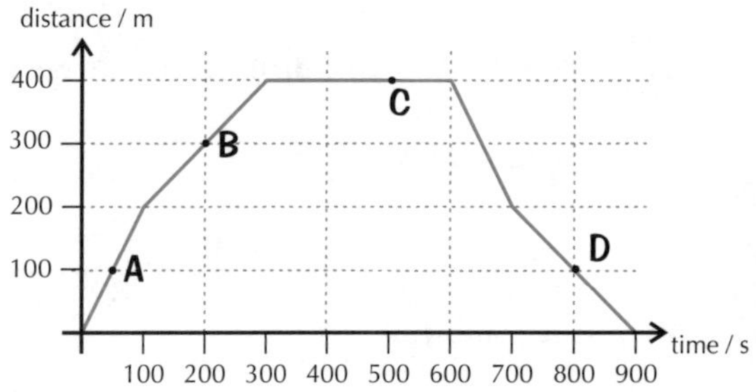

a) How far away was the newsagent's
from Susan's home?

....

b) What was the total distance Susan travelled?

....

c) How much time did Susan spend in the shop?

....

d) Which two points, out of **A**, **B**, **C** and **D**, show Susan walking at the same speed
but with a different velocity?

Points .... and ....

Q5 The speed/time graph below shows two cars (**A** and **B**) accelerating away from traffic lights.

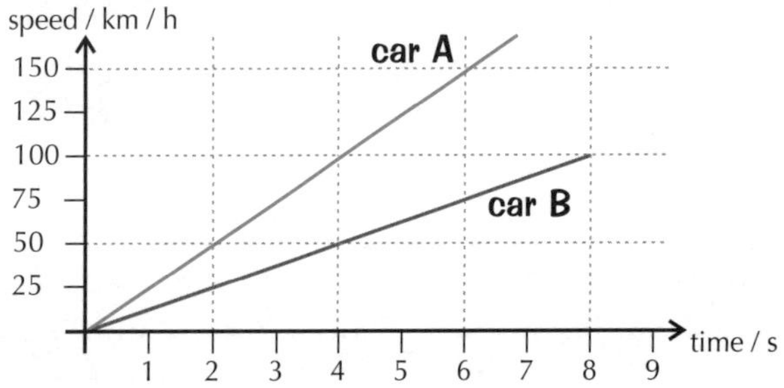

a) How fast was **car A** going at 4 s? ....

b) How fast was **car B** going at this time? ....

c) If the cars were going in the same direction, what would be the speed of car A **relative** to car B (at 4 s)?

....

....

d) If the cars were going in **opposite directions**, what would their relative speed be at 6 seconds?

....

....

Combining Velocities and Forces

Q1 Work out the size and direction of the **resultant force** acting on the pots of jam shown below.

a) 5N ← → 20N

Size of force .... N

Direction: ....

b) 100N ↑
10N ← → 17N
10N ← → 3N
20N ↓

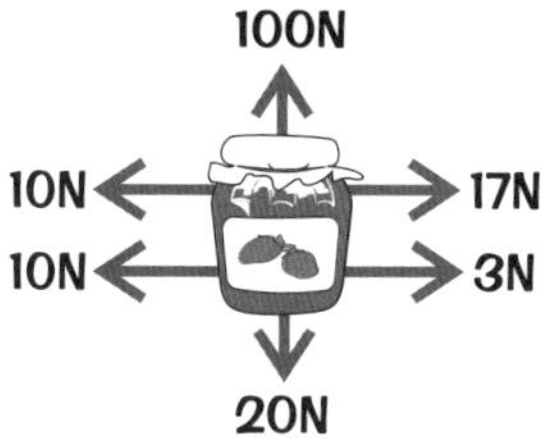

Size of force .... N

Direction: ....

Q2 Greta swims at **1 m/s** to the **East** along a river. Ray stands on the riverbank and watches her.

a) How fast is Greta swimming relative to Ray if the river is flowing at **1.5 m/s due East**?

Velocity = ... m/s   Direction = ...

b) How fast is Greta swimming relative to Ray if the river is flowing **2.0 m/s due West**?

Velocity = ... m/s   Direction = ...

Q3 Forces and velocities can be combined in **vector diagrams**.

a) A glider is flying at **10 m/s due North** when it experiences a cross wind of **15 m/s due East**. Complete the vector diagram and use it to work out the resultant velocity of the glider — its speed and its new bearing (angle clockwise from North). Give your answers to the nearest whole number.

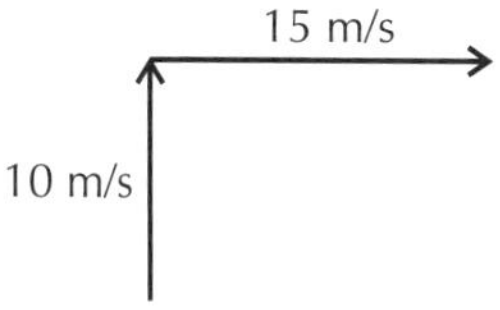

15 m/s

10 m/s

....

....

....

Resultant velocity = ... m/s on a bearing of .... °.

X

b) Emma swims across a river which is flowing westwards at 5 m/s. She swims at 2 m/s, heading directly across the river from point X.

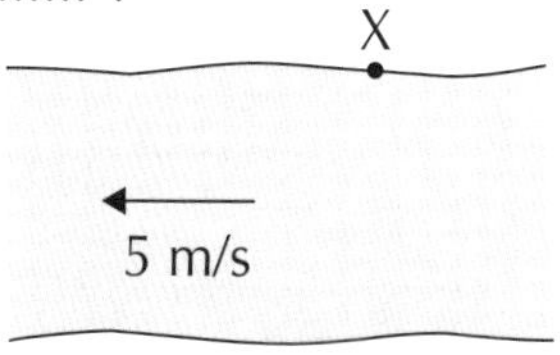

5 m/s

Calculate Emma's resultant velocity — her speed and the angle between her direction of travel and the river bank. Give your answers to the nearest m/s and the nearest degree.

....

....

....

....

Equations of Motion

Q1 a) What quantities do the following symbols stand for in the **equations of motion**?

    i) **s** stands for ....

    ii) **u** stands for ....

    iii) **v** stands for...................................

    iv) **t** stands for ....

    v) **a** stands for ....

You should always stand for the national anthem.

    b) Complete the four equations below.

$$s = ut +$$

$$s = \underline{\quad\quad} \, t$$

$$v = \quad + $$

$$v^2 = $$

Q2 Choose the appropriate equation and solve the following.

You'll need to rearrange the equation for some of these.

    a) Find **s** if u = 0 m/s, a = 5 m/s² and t = 20 s. ....

    b) Find **v** if u = 20 m/s, a = 1 m/s² and s = 250 m. ....

    c) Find **t** if s = 45 m, u = 3 m/s and v = 15 m/s.

    d) Find **a** if s = 100 m, u = 0 m/s and t = 5 s.

Q3 A car accelerates at 2.5 m/s² from rest. What **speed** will it have reached after 20 seconds?

Q4 I throw a banana vertically up into the air at an initial speed of 10 m/s.
It accelerates downwards at 10 m/s². Calculate the **maximum height** of the banana.

Take 'up' as positive and think about the speed the banana is going at when it reaches its maximum height.

Projectile Motion

Q1   Choose from the words below to complete the passage.

> friction   gravity   ground track   parabola   trajectory   hyperbola

The only force acting on a projectile is .... (ignoring air

resistance). The path a projectile follows is called its ....

The shape of this path is a ....

Q2   For each of these statements, tick **true** or **false** as appropriate.

True False

a)   Horizontal and vertical motion are totally separate – one doesn't affect the other.   ☐ ☐

b)   A bullet fired horizontally at 200 m/s will accelerate down to the ground
at the same rate as a stone thrown horizontally at 1 m/s. (Ignore air resistance.)   ☐ ☐

c)   If something is thrown horizontally at 10 m/s, its initial vertical velocity is 10 m/s.   ☐ ☐

d)   The horizontal velocity remains constant for a projectile (ignoring air resistance).   ☐ ☐

e)   On Earth, an object will accelerate vertically towards the ground at about 10 m/s².   ☐ ☐

Q3   This diagram shows a **regular** pulse of water droplets
that have been **projected** through the air.

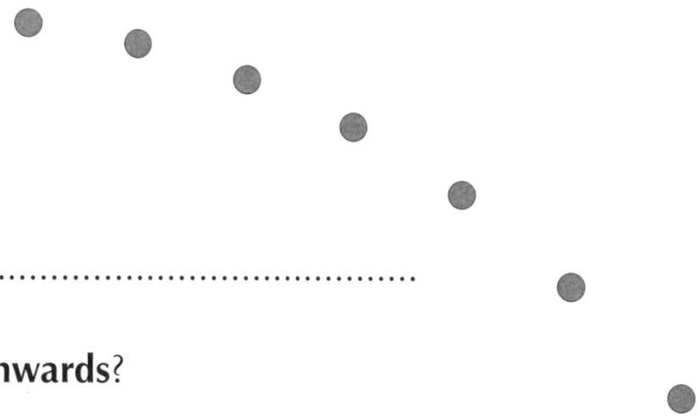

a)   How can you tell from the diagram
that the **horizontal velocity** is **constant**?

....

b)   How can you tell that the droplets are **accelerating downwards**?

....

Q4   Which of the following are examples of projectile motion? Circle any which are.

> a football kicked
> towards the goal

> an orange rolling
> off a table

> a cannonball fired
> from a cannon

> a powered plane
> flying over the Himalayas

> a football dribbled
> towards the goal

> a high jumper in flight

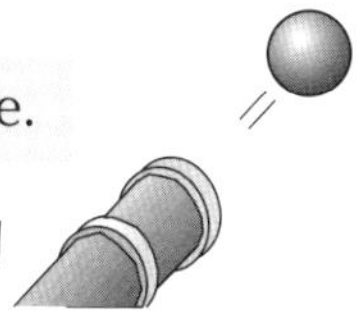

Q5   A plane is carrying some water to try and put out a forest fire.
The plane is flying **horizontally** at a velocity of **80 m/s** and it is **125 m** above the ground.

a)   Taking the acceleration of gravity to be **10 m/s²**, what time will it take the water
to reach the ground once it has left the plane (ignoring air resistance)?

....

....

b)   At what distance before the forest fire must the water be released?

....

Momentum

Q1   Claire (mass 55 kg) is standing on a skateboard (mass 5 kg) at **rest**.
She then **jumps forwards** off the skateboard at 1.8 m/s.

a)   What was the total momentum of Claire and the skateboard before she jumped?

....

b)   What was Claire's momentum after she jumped?

....

c)   Calculate the final momentum of the skateboard.

....

Q2   A 90 g **apple** is fired at 10 m/s from a toy **cannon** which has mass 2 kg.
At what speed will the cannon move backwards?

Watch out for the units.

....

....

....

Q3   Kevin jumped off a high wall. He hit the ground at a velocity of **2 m/s**.
Unfortunately he didn't bend his knees when he landed so it only took
him **0.05 s** to stop moving. Kevin's mass is **60 kg**.

a)   i)   What was Kevin's momentum just before he landed?

....

ii)   Calculate the size of the **force** that acted on Kevin's body.

....

iii)   A year later, when he had recovered from his injuries, Kevin jumped off the same wall again.
This time he bent his knees when he landed and it took him **1 s** to come to a halt.
What force acted on Kevin's body this time?

....

b)   Explain how **airbags**, **crumple zones** and **seatbelts** can reduce the chance of injury in a car crash.

....

....

....

Top Tips: Momentum is like barn owls — it's conserved, as long as no external forces act.
Imagine a stationary barn — zero momentum. Now imagine a bulldozer acting on the barn and
pushing it over — the barn gains some momentum. (And the poor old barn owl loses its home.)

Module P5 — Space for Reflection

Radio Waves and Communication

Q1   Radio waves travel by different routes depending on their **frequency**.
Choose from the words below to fill in the blanks.

> ground   microwaves   long   diffract   ionosphere   curvature   low
> sky   satellites   space   3000 MHz   30 MHz

a)   .... waves travel close to the ground. They have fairly ....
frequencies (up to about 3MHz) and .... wavelengths.

b)   .... waves can reflect off a layer of the atmosphere called the
.... This allows the wave to overcome the .... of the
Earth. These waves have frequencies up to about ....

c)   .... waves pass easily through the atmosphere and reflect off orbiting
.... These waves are actually .... and have frequencies
of over ....

Q2   Long wavelength radio waves carry signals by amplitude modification.

a)   Explain what amplitude modification means.

....

b)   In the space below, sketch the shape of the **signal wave** and **carrier wave** that produced this shape.

Modulated carrier wave 〰〰 =   +

Carrier wave   Signal wave

Q3   One important property of waves is **diffraction**.

a)   Explain what 'diffraction' means.

....

b)   A ripple tank is used to study the behaviour of waves as they pass through gaps. The gap in diagram 1 is about the **same size** as the wavelength. The gap in diagram 2 is **much bigger**.
Complete both diagrams to show what happens to the waves after they pass through the gaps.

① 　　　　　　②

Radio Waves and Communication

Q4   Satellite TV and mobile phone transmissions both use radio waves.

a)   What is the frequency range of radio waves used for satellite TV and mobile phones? Circle the correct letter.

1 GHz = 1000 MHz

     A   500 kHz - 1 MHz   B   1 MHz - 30 MHz   C   30 MHz - 1 GHz

     D   1 GHz - 30 GHz   E   30 GHz - 300 GHz

b)   Hardeep is getting satellite TV installed in his new house. He wants the satellite dish to go on the back of the house. The technician installing the dish explains that the dish **must** go on the **front** of the house, and must point at a specific part of the sky.

     i)   Why must the satellite dish face in a specific direction?

       ....

       ....

     ii)   Describe the path the TV signal takes from the broadcaster's transmitter to Hardeep's house.

       ....

       ....

c)   Explain why only a limited range of radio frequencies can be used to transmit signals from Earth to satellites.

     ....

     ....

Q5   FM radio waves have much **higher frequencies** than long wave radio waves.

a)   Explain why the houses in this picture can receive **long wave** radio but **not FM** radio.

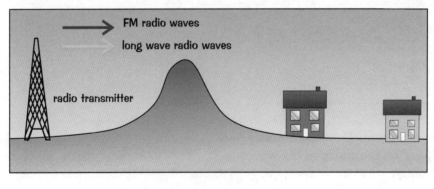

     ....

     ....

b)   A radio station has its studio 10 miles away from its transmitter. Microwaves are used to transmit a signal from the studio to the transmitter. Explain why **microwaves** are used.

     ....

Interference of Waves

Q1 The diagrams below each show **displacement–time graphs** of two waves that are **overlapping**.

On each set of empty axes, draw what the graph of the **combined wave** would look like.
Also decide whether it the interference is **constructive** or **destructive** — circle the correct answer.

a)

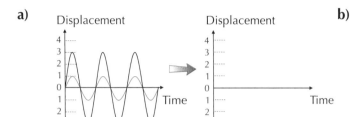

This is **constructive** / **destructive** interference

b)

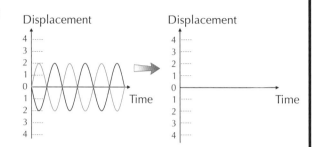

This is **constructive** / **destructive** interference

Q2 Caleb was in a science lesson listening to a single musical note that his teacher
was playing through a loudspeaker. To his surprise, when his teacher
connected up **another speaker**, the sound got **quieter** rather than **louder**.

a) **Explain** what was happening to the two sound waves at the place where Caleb was sitting.

....

....

b) Caleb then got up and walked around the lab. Describe what he might have heard
as he walked around.

....

....

Q3 **Laser light** was shone onto a screen through two very **thin slits** that were close together.

a) Describe what you would see on the screen.

....

b) The slits are much **closer together** than the loudspeakers in Q2. Why is this?

....

....

c) Which of these situations would give **destructive** interference? Circle the correct letter.

A A path difference of an odd number of whole wavelengths

B A path difference of an odd number of half wavelengths

C A path difference of an even number of half wavelengths.

Interference of Waves

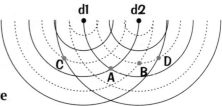

Q4 The diagram shows sets of overlapping waves produced by two dippers (d1 and d2) in a ripple tank. The **solid lines** indicate where there is a **peak** (or crest) and the **dashed lines** indicate where there is a **trough**.

a) For each point A-D decide whether there will be **constructive** or **destructive** interference. Underline the correct answer.

A constructive / destructive **B** constructive / destructive

C constructive / destructive **D** constructive / destructive

b) The wavelength of the waves is **1cm**. Point P is 5 cm away from d1 and 8 cm away from d2.

i) What is the **path difference** at point P? *Point P is not on the diagram, by the way.*

....

ii) How many **half wavelengths** fit into this path difference?

....

iii) Will there be **constructive** or **destructive** interference at point P?

....

c) The dippers were slowed down to produce a wavelength of 2cm.

i) What is the **path difference** at point P now?

....

ii) How many **half wavelengths** fit into this path difference?

....

iii) Will there be **constructive** or **destructive** interference at point P?

....

Q5 A microwave **transmitter**, **receiver** and **reflecting plate** were set up as shown in the diagram.

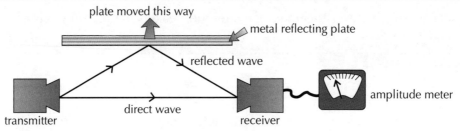

The reflecting plate was moved in the direction shown.
State and explain what was observed on the receiver's meter.

....

....

Diffraction Patterns and Polarisation

Q1 Waves can be either **transverse** or **longitudinal**.

a) State whether the waves on a slinky shown below are transverse or longitudinal.

i)

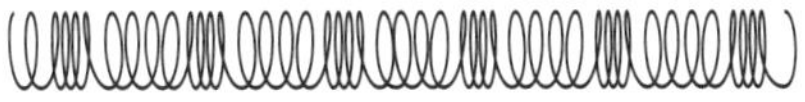

ii)

This is a .... wave   This is a .... wave.

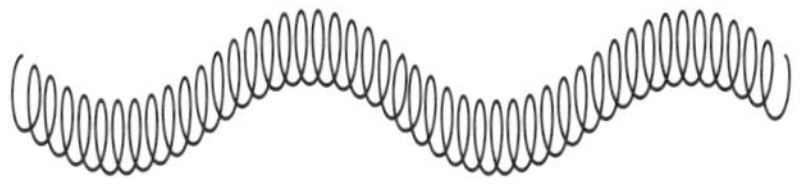

b) Which type of wave is each of the following? Write 'T' for transverse and 'L' for longitudinal.

i) Light ....   **ii)** Water waves ....   **iii)** Sound ....

c) Circle **true** or **false** for each of these statements:

i) Normal light waves are transverse waves vibrating in a mixture of directions. **True / False**

ii) Longitudinal waves can be plane polarised. **True / False**

iii) Plane polarised waves only vibrate in one direction. **True / False**

Q2 A **laser** beam was projected onto a screen through a pair of **Polaroid sunglasses**.
When the glasses were rotated **90°**, they blocked the light completely.

a) What does this tell you about laser light?

....

b) The experiment is repeated using a **torch** instead of a laser.
What would you expect to see now when the sunglasses were rotated 90°?

....

c) The torch beam is then reflected off a **glass plate**
on the bench as shown in the diagram.
What happens now when the sunglasses are rotated?

....

....

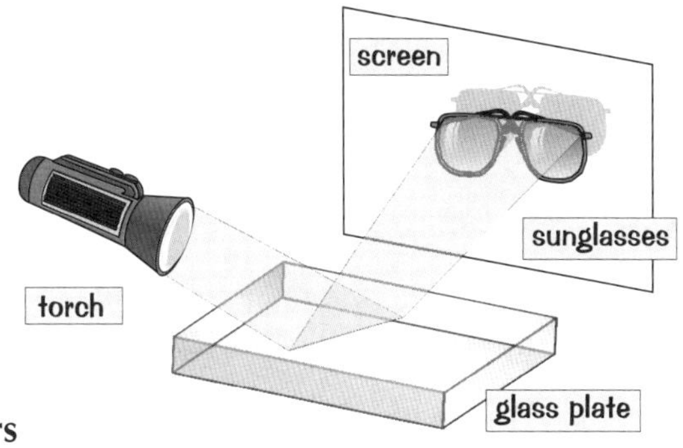

d) Explain why Polaroid sunglasses are useful for **car drivers**
on a sunny day when the roads are wet.

....

....

Q3 A **laser** beam was shone towards a screen through a **small circular hole**.
The pattern shown was seen on the screen. Explain how this pattern is formed.

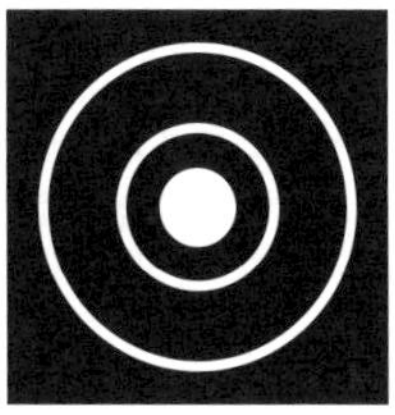

....

....

....

__Refraction__

Q1   Fill in the blanks in the passage below.

> Waves can speed up or .... when they
>
> pass from one medium to another. If they are travelling at an
>
> angle to the .... then the change in
>
> speed results in a change of ....

Q2 a)   What is meant by a "normal line" when talking about refraction?

....

b)   Delete words in the statements below to make them correct.

i) When a wave **slows down**, it may bend towards / away from the normal. The wavelength gets longer / gets shorter / stays the same. The frequency increases / decreases / stays the same.

ii) When a wave **speeds up**, it may bend towards / away from the normal. The wavelength gets longer / gets shorter / stays the same. The frequency increases / decreases / stays the same.

c)   On each diagram, **draw** the ray bending **towards** or **away** from the normal line.

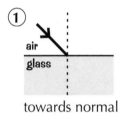

towards normal

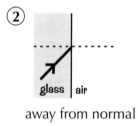

away from normal

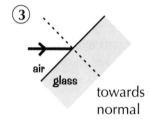

towards normal

Q3   The diagram shows a ray of light entering a rectangular glass block.

a)   Complete the diagram by sketching the path of the ray. Ignore any reflections.

b)   This diagram shows the **wavefronts** of the light in the same situation. Complete the diagram to show what happens to the wavefronts once they have entered the glass block.

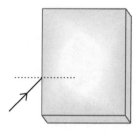

Q4   On a sunny day, bright light shines onto my car window. Not **all** the light waves are refracted on entering the glass. Explain why.

There are two reasons.

....

....

Refraction: Two Special Cases

Q1 A prism can be used to separate **white light** into its different colours.

a) What name is given to the **splitting** of white light into different colours?

....

b) Which colour of the rainbow refracts **least**? ....

c) Which colour of the rainbow refracts **most**? ....

Q2 **Different colours** of light bend by **different amounts** when the light passes from air into glass.

a) The diagram below shows a ray of **red** light and a ray of **blue** light entering a rectangular glass block.

i) Complete the diagram by drawing the rays as they pass completely through the block (ignoring any reflections).

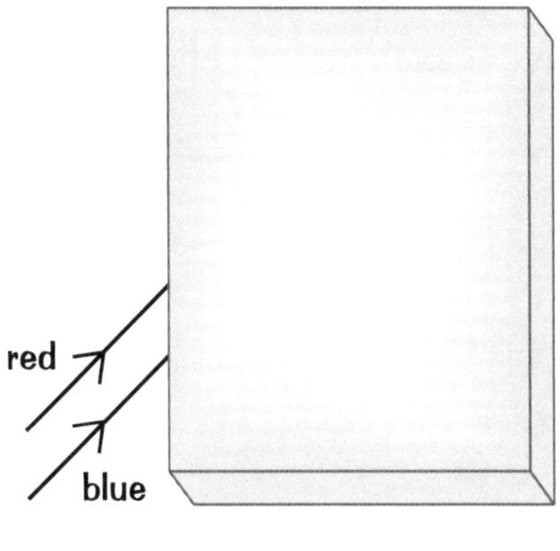

red

blue

ii) Which would be refracted more on entering a similar glass block — ultraviolet or infrared? Circle the correct answer.

ultraviolet   infrared

b) Why do the colours of white light noticeably separate when they pass through a **triangular** block but not through a rectangular one?

....

....

Q3 This question is about **total internal reflection**.

In which of these situations could you get total internal reflection? Circle the correct letter(s).

A Light is coming out of air into water.
B Light is coming out of glass into air.

Explain your answer.

....

....

Refraction: Two Special Cases

Q4 The critical angle for glass/air is 42°.

Complete the ray diagrams below.

You'll need to measure the angle of incidence for each one — carefully.

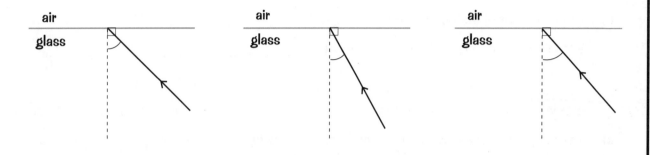

Q5 **Right-angled prisms** can be used in binoculars and periscopes to ensure that light is totally internally reflected.

a) Explain why right angled prisms are so useful in total internal reflection.

....

....

b) Complete the paths of the rays in the diagrams below.

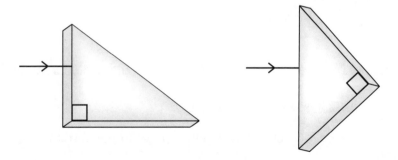

c) The sketch shows a basic periscope which uses two right-angled prisms. Only one of the prisms is shown.

Draw in the other prism and complete the diagram to show the path of the ray.

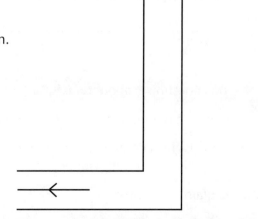

Top Tips: When you're doing total internal reflection, remember that **angles of incidence** are measured from the **normal**, not from the **surface**. Otherwise you'll get it horribly wrong.

Refractive Index and Snell's Law

Q1 Here is a diagram of a ray of light entering a material with **refractive index**, **n**.

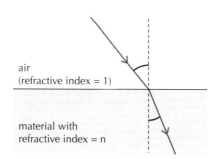

air
(refractive index = 1)

material with
refractive index = n

a) Label the following parts of the diagram:

Incident ray   Normal line Refracted ray

Angle of incidence, i   Angle of refraction, r

b) Snell's law relates the refractive index, **n** to the two angles **i** and **r**. Write down Snell's law.

....

Q2 A light ray was shone from air into some water. The ray had an **angle of incidence** of **30°** and an **angle of refraction** of **22°**. Use this data to calculate the **refractive index** of water.

....

....

....

Q3 A student was investigating the refractive index of a transparent material. She shone yellow light at various **angles of incidence (i)** and measured the **angles of refraction (r)**. She then filled in the table below:

i	r	sin i	sin r
10.0°	8.3°		
20.0°	16.4°		
30.0°	24.8°		
40.0°	32.3°		
50.0°	39.8°		
60.0°	46.2°		

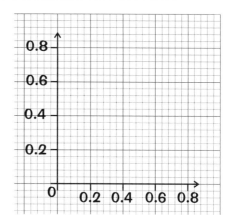

a) **Complete** the table and then draw a graph of **sin r** on the **y-axis** against **sin i** on the **x-axis**.

b) Explain why the **gradient** of the graph = **1/n**, where n is the refractive index of the material.

....

....

c) Use your graph to calculate the refractive index of the material for yellow light.

....

Refractive Index and Snell's Law

Q4 The diagram shows **white light** undergoing dispersion when it refracts from **air** into **glass**.

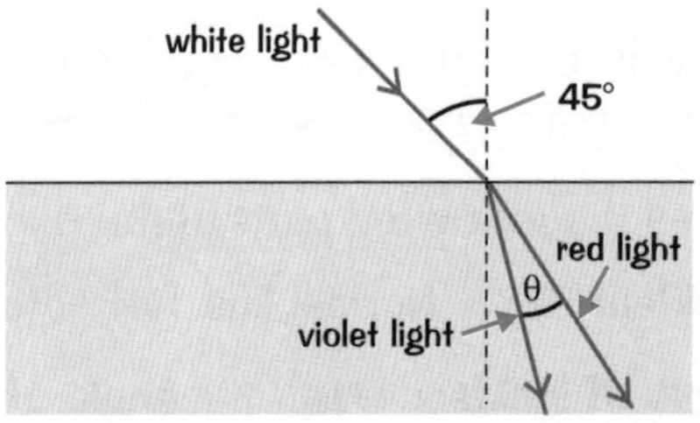

white light   45°

red light

θ

violet light

a) The refractive index in glass for red light is 1.514.
Calculate the **angle of refraction** for red light.

....

....

b) The refractive index in glass for violet light is 1.528.
What does this tell you about the **speed** of **violet** light in glass compared to **red** light?

....

c) Calculate the angle θ shown in the diagram.

....

....

Q5 Light passes through the acrylic bottom of a boat into the water below.
For blue light, the refractive index of **acrylic** is **1.498** (to 3 significant figures)
and the refractive index of **water** is **1.337** (to 3 significant figures).

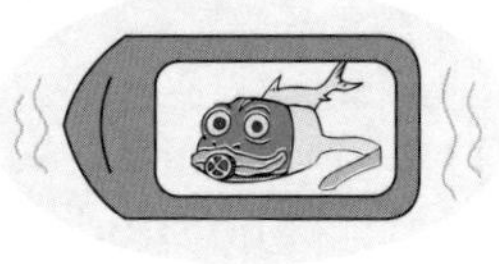

a) i) What happens to the **speed** of the light as it passes into the water?

....

ii) Complete this sentence by underlining the correct option.
The angle of refraction is greater than / less than **the angle of incidence.**

b) If the angle of incidence were equal to the critical angle, what would the **angle** of **refraction** be?

....

c) What happens to light which enters the water at an angle **greater** than the critical angle?

....

d) Calculate the **critical angle** for the **acrylic to water** boundary
for blue light, to the nearest degree.

You'll need the equation with sin C in it.

....

....

....

....

Images and Converging Lenses

Q1 Images can be either **real** or **virtual**.
Tick the appropriate box for each statement below.

Real Virtual

a) Which kind of image **can't** be formed on a screen? ☐ ☐

b) Light rays only **appear** to come from this type of image. ☐ ☐

c) Light rays **actually** come from this type of image. ☐ ☐

d) This is the kind of image you get when you use a lens as a **magnifying glass**. ☐ ☐

Q2 Choose from the words below to complete the passage.

length concave converges axis parallel turning focal distance convex focus

A converging lens has a .... shape (fatter in the middle than the

edges). It brings light rays together (or .... them) to a point called a

.... When the rays are .... to each other and to the

.... of the lens, then the point where the lens brings them together

is called the .... point. The distance between the centre of the lens

and the focal point is called the focal .... of the lens.

Q3 This lens is forming an **image** on a screen.

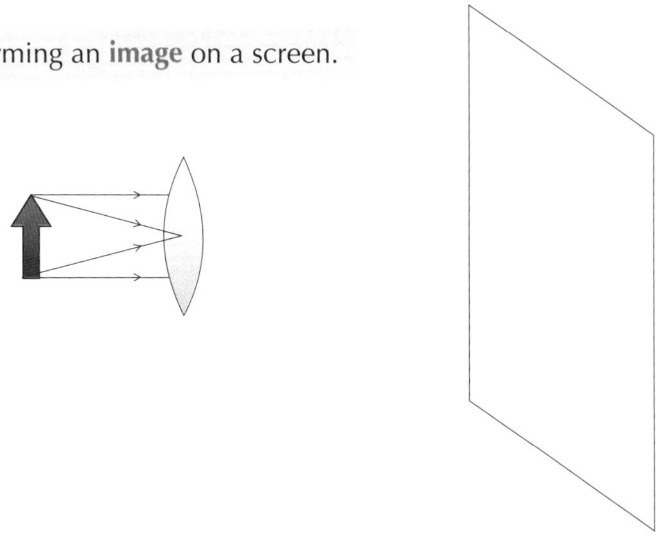

The rays passing through the centre of the lens don't bend.

a) Complete the paths of the rays in the diagram and draw in the image.

b) Circle the correct options in the following sentences.

i) The image is bigger / smaller than the object.

ii) The image is upright / inverted.

iii) The image is real / virtual.

Images and Converging Lenses

Q4   The diagram below shows another way you can use a **converging lens** to form an image.

a)   Complete the diagram to show where the image is formed.

b)   Give a **full description** of the image.

Use the rays that are already there to help you figure it out.

1. ....

2. ....

3. ....

4. ....

c)   Give a possible application for this type of lens used in this way.

....

Q5 a)   On the diagrams below, **label** the following:

Parallel light   **Diverging light**   **Focal point**   **Converging light**   **Focal length**

b)   **i)**   Which lenses are more powerful — fatter lenses or thinner lenses?

....

ii)   How does the focal length of a lens depend on its shape?

....

c)   The diagrams below show parallel rays being converged by two different lenses. Draw in the lenses making sure you show how their shapes are different.

i)

ii)

Top Tips: Remember all the things that you need to write down to describe an image formed by a lens. Make sure you can label an image with focal point, focal length, etc — piddly little things like this could be worth a few marks come exam time. It all adds up.

Ray Diagrams

Q1   This question is about how to **draw ray diagrams**.

a)   The first step is to draw a ray from the **top** of the object going **parallel** to the **axis** of the lens. Where does this ray pass through when it's refracted?

....

b)   The next step is to draw a ray from the top of the object which passes through the lens **without** being refracted. Where does this ray pass through the lens?

....

c)   How do the steps above tell you where the **top** of the **image** will be on the ray diagram?

....

Q2   Draw a ray diagram to locate where the image is by **following the instructions** below.

a)   Draw a ray from the **top** of the object (towards the lens) **parallel** to the axis, and continue the path of the ray through the lens.

b)   Draw a ray from the top of the object passing through the **centre** of the lens.

c)   Mark the **top** of the image

d)   Mark the **bottom** of the image, and draw in the image.

Take these ray diagrams step by step. Make sure you draw them really carefully, with a ruler.

e)   Now **describe** the image fully.

....

....

....

....

Ray Diagrams

Q3 Complete this ray diagram so that you can **fully describe** the image that this lens produces.

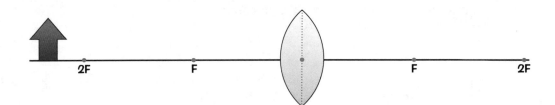

Description of image: ....

....

....

Q4 Complete this ray diagram so that you can **fully describe** the image that this lens produces.

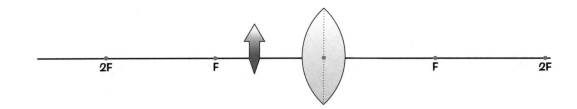

Description of image: ....

....

....

Q5 Here is a ray diagram of a lens and an object that is **one focal length** away from the lens.

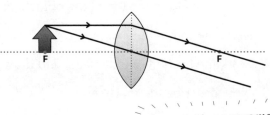

Where do these rays meet?

  a) How far away would the image be?
Explain your answer.

....

....

  b) How far away would an object have to be in order to produce an image at the focal point on the **right hand side** of the lens?

....

Uses — Magnification and Cameras

Q1 Magnifying glasses use convex lenses to produce images which are **larger** than the object.

a) What is the **furthest distance** the object can be from the lens when a convex lens is used as a magnifier?

....

b) Will the image be a **real** image or a **virtual** one? ....

c) What **test** could you do to check whether the image is real or virtual?

....

Q2 The magnification of a lens system can be worked out using the **heights** of the **object** and the **image**.

a) Write down the formula relating magnification, object height and image height.

....

b) A **1.5 cm** stamp was observed through a magnifying glass. The virtual image it produced was **6 cm** high. What was the magnification?

....

c) A camera was used to take the picture of a tree. If the magnification was **0.002** and the image of the tree was **2 cm** high, what was the **actual height** of the tree?

....

Q3 **Complete** the ray diagram and **take measurements** to find the magnification of this system.

Draw the diagram REALLY carefully.

....

....

Uses – Magnification and Cameras

Q4 Lenses are used in **cameras**.

a) Delete the incorrect words in these statements about a camera
being used to take a normal family photo.

The magnification is **less than 1 / exactly 1 / less than 1.**

The image is **real / virtual.**

The image is **upside down / the right way up.**

b) Here is a ray diagram for a camera taking a photo of a flower.

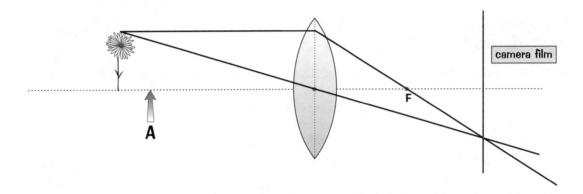

camera film

A

F

The flower is moved closer to the lens as shown by the arrow A in the diagram.
Draw in a new ray diagram to show how where the new image be.

c) What would you have to do to the camera, to keep the image focussed on the film?

....

Q5 This question is about the uses of **lenses** in **film projectors**.

a) Cross out the incorrect words in these statements about lenses in film projectors.

The magnification is **less than 1 / exactly 1 / more than 1.**

The image is **real / virtual.**

The image is **upside down / the right way up.**

b) **Which way up** must the **film** (the object) go in order
to produce the correct image on the cinema screen?

....

c) A film projector was moved from one cinema to another cinema where the screen was
further away from the projector. How should the distance between the **film** and the **lens** be
changed in order to focus the picture correctly on the cinema screen?

....

Mixed Questions — Module P5

Q1 There are hundreds of **satellites** orbiting the Earth.

a) The path on the Earth's surface directly beneath a satellite is called its **ground track**. This flattened out map of the Earth shows the ground track of a **polar orbiting satellite**.

On the same diagram, draw and label a possible ground track of a **geostationary** satellite.

←— ground track of polar satellite
—— Equator

b) Satellite X is in low polar orbit about 7200 km away from the centre of the Earth. Geostationary satellites are about 42 000 km from the centre of the Earth.

i) Satellite X experiences a centripetal force of approximately 3.1×10^4 N. Calculate the force the same satellite would experience if it were in a **geostationary orbit**.

....

....

ii) Satellite X completes one orbit approximately every 100 minutes. Calculate its speed, giving your answer in km/h.

You'll need to work out the circumference of the orbit.

....

....

Q2 Isabel and Josie are having a clarinet lesson with their teacher Mrs Stave. The window is open because it's a hot day. Josie's mum walks past and thinks that the music sounds muffled.

a) Use your knowledge of **diffraction** to explain why Josie's mum can't hear the **high-pitched** sounds.

....

....

b) Before playing a duet Isobel and Josie checked the tuning of their instruments.

i) The girls played the same note, starting at exactly the same time. As Mrs Stave paced up and down the room, she found that the note sounded very loud in some places (L) and very quiet in others (Q).

Explain why Mrs Stave hears these differences in the note as she walks.

Isabel ●   **S** •L ↘ •Q •L Josie ● •Q •L

Think about how the waves are interfering.

NOT TO SCALE

....

....

....

ii) The diagram shows the sound wave Mrs Stave heard from Isobel's clarinet when she was at point **S** (see above).

Josie played more loudly than Isobel. On the same diagram sketch the wave Mrs Stave heard from **Josie's** clarinet.

Displacement / Time

Mixed Questions — Module P5

Q3 Anna and Bert are flying their remote-controlled planes, as shown.

a) What is plane A's velocity
relative to plane B? .... m/s.

25 m/s   270 m   20 m/s
A   B

b) Both planes are flying 8 m above the ground.
If a screw falls off plane A, how long will it take to reach the ground? (Use **g** = 9.81 m/s².)

....

c) i) If the planes continue at the velocities shown, how long will it be before they collide?

....

ii) Plane A's mass is 600 g. Plane B's mass is 850 g. If they collided and stuck together without suffering any damage, what would the velocities of the planes be immediately **after** the collision?

....

....

....

d) Bert directs his plane upwards to avert a collision. It is then affected by a wind blowing at 50 km/h north. His plane was previously flying west at 20 m/s. Work out its new speed.

....

....

Q4 Andrew is looking at a shell. He can see it because the lens in his eye forms an image on his **retina**.

a) Complete the paths of the light rays on the diagram.

retina

b) Andrew uses a **magnifying glass** to examine the shell,
lens
which is 1.8 cm tall. He finds that to magnify the shell,
he must hold the lens less than 3 cm from it. When he holds the magnifying glass 2.5 cm away from the shell, the image formed is 4 cm tall.

i) What is the focal length of this lens? ....

ii) What is the magnification of the lens at 2.5 cm? ....

Q5 The diagram shows light incident on a **bicycle reflector**.

a) Sketch the paths of the two light rays after they hit the reflector.

red plastic

b) The refractive index of the transparent plastic is 1.6.
How fast does the light travel in the transparent plastic?
(The speed of light in a vacuum is 3×10^8 m/s.)

transparent
plastic

....

Module P5 — Space for Reflection

Circuits — The Basics

Q1   Fill in the gaps in the sentences below.

a)   The flow of electrons round a circuit is called the ....

b)   .... is the 'force' that pushes the current round the circuit.

c)   If you increase the voltage, ... current will flow.

d)   If you increase the ...., less current will flow.

Q2   Match up these items from a standard test circuit with the **correct description** and **symbol**.

ITEM	DESCRIPTION	
Cell	The item being tested.	
Variable Resistor	Provides the voltage.	
Component	Used to alter the current.	
Voltmeter	Measures the current.	
Ammeter	Measures the voltage.	

Q3 a)   Write down the **units** of each of the following quantities:

   i) current ....   **ii)** voltage ....   **iii)** resistance ....

b)   Write down two ways of **decreasing** the current in a standard test circuit.

   1. ....

   2. ....

Q4   Indicate whether these statements are **true** or **false**.
Write out correct versions of the false statements.

                                                                                                True False

a)   Current flows from positive to negative.   ☐   ☐

   ....

b)   An ammeter should be connected in parallel with a component.   ☐   ☐

   ....

c)   A voltmeter should be connected in series with a component.   ☐   ☐

   ....

Q5   Five pupils designed circuits to collect data for plotting a V-I graph for a component. Unfortunately, some of their circuits will **not** allow them to collect the data they need. Circle the **incorrect** circuits.

Voltage-Current Graphs and Resistance

Q1   Draw **circuit symbols** for each of these components. The first one has been done for you.

a) Diode   **b)** Switch (open)   **c)** Variable resistor   **d)** Battery   **e)** Bulb

Q2   Circle the correct words in the following statements.

a)   The resistance of a filament lamp **increases / decreases** as it gets hotter.

b)   The steeper the gradient of a V-I graph, the **higher / lower** the resistance is.

c)   The current through a resistor at constant temperature is
directly / inversely proportional to the voltage.

Q3   The diagram shows an old fashioned **variable resistor**
with a large coil of wire and a sliding contact,
connected in series to a **battery** and a **motor**.

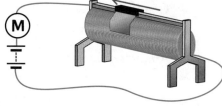

a)   How would the resistance of the variable resistor change
if you moved the contact to the left (as shown)?

....

b)   What would happen to the **speed** of the **motor** if you moved the contact to the left (as shown)?

....

Q4   The graph below shows **V-I curves** for four resistors.

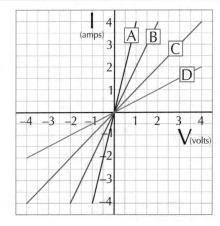

Gradient = $\dfrac{\text{vertical change}}{\text{horizontal change}}$

a)   Which resistor has the highest resistance? ....

b)   Calculate the gradient of the line for resistor B.

....

c)   Calculate the resistance of resistor B.

....

Q5   The graph shows a V-I curve for a **filament lamp**.

Explain why the graph curves.

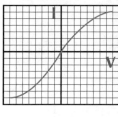

Think about what happens to
the filament of the lamp when it
has a large voltage across it.

....

....

....

Potential Dividers

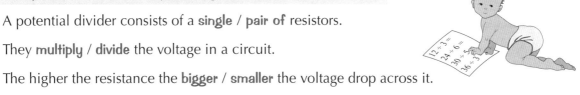

Q1   Complete the sentences by circling the correct word or words.

a)   A potential divider consists of a **single** / **pair of** resistors.

b)   They **multiply** / **divide** the voltage in a circuit.

c)   The higher the resistance the **bigger** / **smaller** the voltage drop across it.

Q2   Tick to show whether the following statements are **true** or **false**.

                                                                                                         True False

a)   The voltage at the point between the resistors is the output of the potential divider.

b)   The output voltage can have any value.

c)   If the resistors are equal then the output voltage will be 50% of the total voltage.

d)   To vary the output, both the resistors must be variable resistors.

Q3   The diagram shows a potential divider consisting of resistors R_1 and R_2. Complete the statements below about how the output voltage can be **varied**.

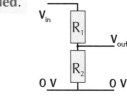

a)   If the output voltage is too low you could **increase** it by .... the resistance of resistor **R_1**.

b)   If the output voltage is too high you could **decrease** it by .... the resistance of resistor ....

Q4   The diagram shows a potential divider. Calculate the **output voltage** V_{out} for each of the following sets of values for R_1 and R_2.

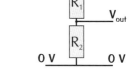

a) $R_1 = R_2 = 10\ \Omega$. ....

....

b) $R_1 = 20\ \Omega$. $R_2 = 10\ \Omega$. ....

....

c) $R_1 = 10\ \Omega$. $R_2 = 20\ \Omega$. ....

....

Q5   A pair of resistors, R_1 and R_2, makes up a potential divider. The total **input voltage** is **6 V**. The graph shows how the **output voltage** changes as R_1 is changed.

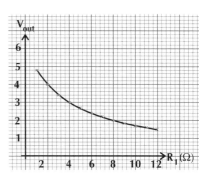

a)   What value of R_1 gives an output voltage of **2.2 V**? ....

b)   What value of R_1 gives an output voltage of **6.0V**? ....

c)   Use the graph to find the value of **R_2**.

....

LDRs and Thermistors

Q1 Cross out the **incorrect** word from each pair to make the following statements true.

a) An LDR has a high resistance in very bright / dim light.

b) A thermistor gets more / less resistive as the temperature drops.

Q2 After each sentence, write **LDR**, **thermistor**, or **both** as appropriate.

a) Changes its resistance in response to conditions around it. ....

b) Could be used as part of a thermostat. ....

c) Would have a high resistance in a warm dark room. ....

d) Would have a low resistance in a warm dark room. ....

Q3 A **motor** rotates the blades of a fan. The motor is in series with an **LDR** as shown in this circuit diagram.

a) What happens to the speed of the fan in the room as the light fades?

....

b) Why does this happen?

....

Q4 An electrical thermometer includes the potential divider shown.

a) At 30°C the resistance of the thermistor is 10 kΩ. What would the **output voltage** be at 30°C?

....

b) What would happen to the **resistance** of the thermistor if the room got **warmer**?

....

c) What would happen to the **output voltage** if the room got **colder**?

....

Q5 Look at the **components** on the right.

Draw your circuit here

a) Use **some** of the components to design a circuit that will vary the brightness of a **lamp** depending on the **temperature** in the room.

b) What happens to the **resistance** in the circuit as the room temperature **increases**? ....

c) What happens to the **brightness** of the lamp as the room temperature **decreases**?

....

Module P6 — Electricity for Gadgets

Magnetic Fields

Q1 Fill in the word **North** or **South** in the following sentences.

a) A .... pole will repel a North pole.

b) Field lines always point towards a .... pole.

c) Reversing the current in a solenoid will turn a .... pole into a South pole.

d) A .... pole is found when a current appears to go clockwise in a coil.

Q2 The diagram below shows a **wire** carrying a current passing through a piece of **flat card**.

a) Some **iron filings** are sprinkled onto the card. When the current is switched on, a pattern develops in the iron filings.

On the diagram, sketch the pattern the iron filings make, including arrows to show the direction of the magnetic field.

Remember the direction of conventional current flow. Then use your hand...

piece of card

3 V battery

switch

b) A loop of current-carrying wire as shown has a **stronger** magnetic field **inside** the loop than outside. Explain why this is, including a sketch of the magnetic field.

....

....

....

Q3 Tick to show whether the following are **true** or **false**. Write a correct version of each false statement.

	True	False
a) Inside a coil the magnetic field is just like a bar magnet.	☐	☐
b) Iron keeps its magnetism when the current is switched off.	☐	☐
c) As more turns are added to a coil its magnetic field gets weaker.	☐	☐
d) Adding a soft iron core will increase the strength of the solenoid's magnetic field.	☐	☐

Module P6 — Electricity for Gadgets

Magnetic Fields

Q4   The diagram below shows a **coil of wire** carrying a current (a **solenoid**).

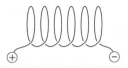

a)   Draw the shape of the magnetic field around the coil.

b)   Indicate on the diagram the **North** and **South** poles of the solenoid.

c)   What effect would the solenoid have on a piece of soft iron placed near one of its ends?

....

d)   Sarah holds a bar magnet with its North pole nearest to the left hand end of the coil in the diagram. The bar magnet experiences a force.

    i)   In what direction would the force on the bar magnet be — towards the coil or away from it?

....

    ii)   Suggest **two** different ways in which the direction of this force could be reversed.

....

....

Q5   Explain why the following are **bad ideas**.

a)   Making an electromagnetic crane out of a **magnetically hard** material, like steel.

....

....

b)   Reversing the current in **both** of a pair of solenoids to stop them repelling each other.

....

....

Top Tips: Make sure you always draw **magnetic field arrows** going the right way. It's easy to lose marks on fiddly bits like that when you aren't paying attention. And don't go using the wrong **hand** to work out the field around a current-carrying wire — cos you'll get it **wrong** if you do that.

Module P6 — Electricity for Gadgets

The Motor Effect

Q1 Complete the passage below using the words supplied.

force	field	angle	stronger	permanent	current	magnetic	magnets

A wire carrying an electric current has a .... around it.

This can react with the magnetic fields of other wires or of ....

.... to produce a .... and sometimes movement. A bigger

.... or a .... magnet will produce a bigger force. The size of

the force also depends on the .... at which the two magnetic fields meet.

Q2 The diagram shows an electrical wire between two magnetic poles.
When the current is switched on, the wire moves at **right angles** to the magnetic field.

a) Which way will the wire move?

....

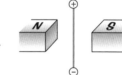

b) How could the wire be made to
move in the opposite direction? ....

c) Explain **why** the wire moves.

....

....

Q3 This experiment was set up to illustrate the motor effect.
When the current is switched on the bar rolls along the rails.

a) Which of the statements A to D below states correctly
what the experiment shows? Circle the appropriate letter.

A A force acts in the same direction as the current is flowing.
B The magnetic field from the magnet combines with the field from the current in the bar.
C The horseshoe magnet pushes the bar along.
D The current in the bar pulls it along the rails.

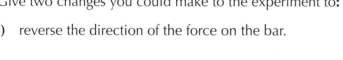

b) Give two changes you could make to the experiment to:

i) reverse the direction of the force on the bar.

....

....

ii) increase the magnitude of the force on the bar.

....

The Simple Electric Motor

Q1 Which of the following will make an electric motor spin **faster**? Circle the relevant letter(s).

   A   Having more turns on the coil.

   B   Using a stronger magnetic field.

   C   Using a soft iron core.

   D   Using a bigger current.

   E   Using a commutator.

Q2 Read the three statements below. Tick the box next to each statement that you think is **true**.

   ☐ The split ring commutator makes the motor spin faster.

   ☐ The split ring commutator reverses the direction of the current every half turn by
        swapping the contacts to the DC supply.

   ☐ The split ring commutator reverses the polarity of the DC supply every half turn.

Q3 State two ways in which the direction of spin of a simple DC motor can be reversed.

   1. ....

   2. ....

Q4 The diagram shows a current-carrying coil in a magnetic field.

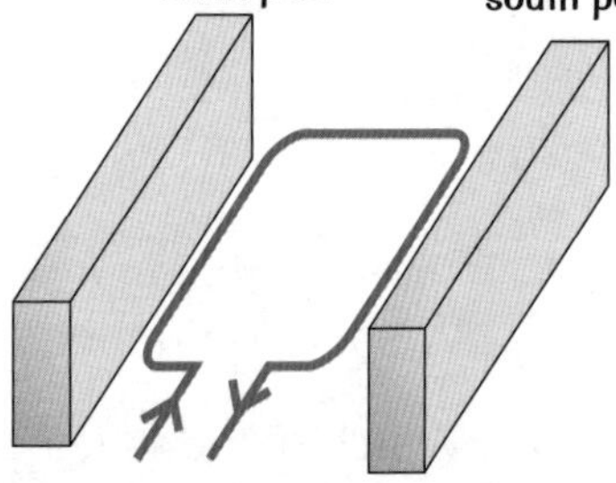

   a) Draw an arrow on the diagram to show
          the direction of the magnetic field.

   b) Describe the direction of the force on the **left-hand** arm of the coil.

          ....

   c) In which direction will the coil move — **clockwise** or **anticlockwise**? ....

   d) **i)** This diagram shows the coil just after it has turned
               through **90°**. Draw arrows to show the direction of the
               forces on each arm of the coil at this stage and describe
               how you would expect the coil to move.

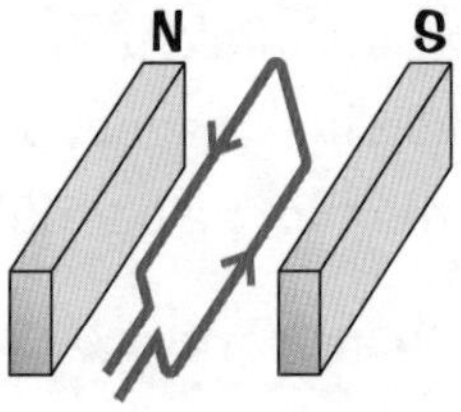

               ....

       ii) In a motor, the coil keeps rotating in the same direction. Explain how this is achieved.

               ....

               ....

   e) In a practical motor, the poles of the magnet are strongly **curved.** Explain why.

          ....

Electromagnetic Induction

Q1 a) Write down a **definition** of electromagnetic induction.

....

....

b) What is another name for electromagnetic induction?

....

Q2 Look at the apparatus shown in the diagram.

Centre-reading ammeter

N   S

Electrical wire

a) Describe how you could use the apparatus to demonstrate **electromagnetic induction**.

....

....

b) What you would see on the ammeter?

....

....

c) What effect, if any, would the following have:

i) swapping the magnetic poles?

....

ii) reversing the connections to the ammeter?

....

Q3 Tick the boxes to show whether the following are **true** or **false**.

		True	False
a)	You can induce a voltage in a wire by moving the wire back and forth near a magnet.	☐	☐
b)	You can induce a voltage in a wire by moving a magnet back and forth near a wire.	☐	☐
c)	If you keep moving a wire back and forth in a magnetic field you will get a DC current.	☐	☐
d)	The faster you move a wire back and forth in a magnetic field, the higher the voltage .	☐	☐

Electromagnetic Induction

Q4   A **simple generator** can be made by rotating a magnet end to end inside a coil of wire.

a)   What happens to the magnetic field after the magnet has turned half a turn?

....

b)   What is initially created in the wire by this rotation?

....

c)   If you keep turning the magnet in the same direction, will this generate an
alternating current (AC) or a direct current (DC) in the wire?   ....

Q5   Moving a **magnet** inside an electric **coil** produces a trace on a cathode ray oscilloscope.

When the magnet was pushed inside the coil, Trace A was produced on the screen.

a)   Explain how Trace B could be produced.

....

b)   Explain how Trace C could be produced.

....

c)   Explain how Trace D could be produced.

....

d)   Explain how energy is transferred from the moving magnet to the oscilloscope.

....

....

Top Tips: Some of this will be familiar from module P2. It's worth making doubly sure you
know it, because you might get harder exam questions on it for this module than for P2.

Module P6 — Electricity for Gadgets

Generators

Q1 Choose from the words below to complete the passage.

brushes	field	current	direction	drier	half	full	motors	slip	split	magnetic	tumble

In a generator, a coil is made to turn inside a ....

.... As the coil spins a .... is induced in

it. Instead of a split ring commutator, an AC generator has ....

rings and .... AC generators produce current which changes

.... every .... turn of the coil.

Q2 **Dynamos** are similar to generators.

a) Which part of a dynamo **rotates**? ....

b) What type of **current** does a dynamo generate? ....

c) How is the rotating part of a cycle dynamo turned?

....

d) What **problem** might there be in having a dynamo lighting a cycle lamp:

i) in very hilly country? ....

....

ii) at traffic lights? ....

....

Q3 **Slip-rings** are an important part of both generators and dynamos.

a) Which of the statements below about slip rings in a generator are **true**?
Tick the appropriate box(es).

☐ The slip rings enable the current to enter and leave
the coils of the generator while it is turning.

☐ The slip rings reverse the direction of the current
supplied to an external circuit every half turn.

☐ The slip rings provide current to an external circuit
in the opposite direction every full turn.

*Think about what split-ring
commutators actually do.*

b) Why don't **AC generators** have **split-ring commutators**?

....

....

Generators

Q4 Here is a **CRO display** of the voltage produced by a **generator**.

The displays below show the voltage produced under **different conditions**.

Traces on oscilloscope

     A   **B**   **C**   **D**

Pick the correct letter A-D to show:

a) The generator turning **twice as fast**. ....

b) The generator turning **more slowly** than originally. ....

c) The generator turning at the **same speed** as originally but with **stronger magnets**. ....

Q5 Here is another **CRO display** of the voltage produced by an AC generator.

Point **X** on the diagram happened when the coil was like **this** in the magnetic field.

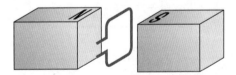

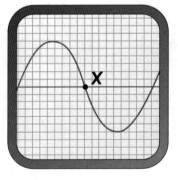

a) Mark **the** letter **Y** on the diagram of the display to show **another** point when the coil is in a similar position.

This diagram shows the coil in another position in the magnetic field.

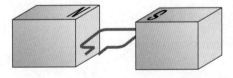

Think about how much the position of the coil has changed.

b) Mark the letter **Z** on the diagram of the display to show a point where the coil is like **this** in the magnetic field.

c) On the CRO screen to the right, draw a trace to show how the voltage would change if the generator's **slip rings** were changed for a **split ring commutator**.

Transformers

Q1 The following statements are **false**. Below each statement, write a correct version.

a) Transformers can work with AC or DC.

....

b) A transformer consists of a laminated iron core and one wire coil.

....

c) Step up transformers have more turns on the primary coil than the secondary coil.

....

d) Eddy currents make a transformer more efficient.

....

Q2 Number the following statements in the right order to explain how a transformer works.

	This causes a rapidly-changing magnetic field in the core.
	An alternating current can flow in a circuit connected to the secondary coil.
	An alternating current flows in the primary coil.
1	An alternating voltage is connected to the primary coil of a transformer.
	The changing magnetic field induces an alternating voltage in the secondary coil.

Q3 Transformers have a **laminated iron core**.

a) Why is the iron core **laminated**?

....

....

b) Explain why a voltage is induced in the **secondary coil** when an alternating current flows in the primary coil.

....

....

c) Why do transformers work with **alternating** current **only**?

....

....

138

Transformers

Q4 Ash, Lisa and Sara are discussing transformers.

Ash says: "The core of a transformer has to be made of a conducting material such as iron so the current can get through."

Lisa says: "There can never be any electric current at all in the core."

Sara says: "Energy must pass through the core."

Who is right and who is wrong? Give reasons for your answers.

a) Ash is .... because ....

....

b) Lisa is .... because ....

....

c) Sara is .... because ....

....

Q5 Tim is investigating a transformer. He uses it to power a **spotlight**, and measures the **voltage** and **current** for both the **primary** and **secondary** coils. Here are his results.

Voltage to primary coil (V)	Current in primary coil (A)	Voltage to secondary coil (V)	Current in secondary coil (A)
240	0.25	12	5.0

a) Is Tim's transformer a **step-up** or **step-down** transformer? Give a reason for your answer.

....

b) i) Calculate the power in the **primary** coil when using the spotlight.

....

ii) Calculate the power the **secondary** coil when using the spotlight.

....

c) What idea about the **efficiency** of a transformer is confirmed by Tim's results?

....

Top Tips: Transformers — so much fun they had a whole cartoon series made about them. They had a nice **equation** made about them too — which awaits you on the next two pages. You'll also need to understand **why** transformers need AC current, and why they have laminated iron cores.

Module P6 — Electricity for Gadgets

Transformers

Q6 Match up these **voltages** to the places where they are found on the National Grid.

VOLTAGE	FOUND
230 V	Long-distance cables carried on pylons.
25 000 V	From power stations.
33 000 V	Homes and factories.
400 000 V	Local underground high-voltage cables.

Q7 Transformers are very important for power transmission in the National Grid.

a) Fill in the blanks in the passage by choosing from the words below.

increase   generate   decrease   step-up   step-down   pipes   cables

.... transformers are used near power stations to .... the voltage. The power is then carried through .... to near homes and factories where .... transformers .... the voltage.

b) Indicate whether these statements are **true** or **false**. Write out a correction if the statement is false.

i) In transmission cables, higher voltage means lower current. **T / F**

....

ii) In transmission cables the energy lost is proportional to the current. **T / F**

....

Q8 In one electricity distribution circuit, the cables carry a current of **200 A** at a voltage of **132 kV**.

a) Calculate the **power** transmitted by this circuit.

....

b) If a transformer is used to step the voltage down to 11 kV, what will the **current** then be?

....

....

c) Explain fully why the National Grid transmits electricity at **high voltage**.

....

....

....

d) Why does the National Grid need big pylons with huge insulators?

....

Module P6 — Electricity for Gadgets

Transformers

Q9   Use the **transformer equation** to complete the following table.

Number of turns on primary coil	Voltage to primary coil (V)	Number of turns on secondary coil	Voltage to secondary coil (V)
1000	12	4000	
1000		2000	20
1000	12		12
	33 000	500	230

Q10   **Isolating transformers** are safety devices.

a)   Which sentence correctly states the relationship between the primary and secondary coils of an isolating transformer? Circle the correct letter.

A An isolating transformer has **more** turns on the **primary** coil than on the secondary coil.

B An isolating transformer has **equal** numbers of turns on the primary and secondary coils.

C An isolating transformer has **more** turns on the **secondary** coil than on the primary coil.

b)   Do isolating transformers change the **voltage** in a circuit? ....

c)   Explain why an isolating transformer is often used in a **bathroom shaver circuit**.

....

....

....

Q11   A transformer has **5000** turns on its **primary** coil and **8000** turns on its **secondary** coil.

a)   If the input voltage is 230 V, find the output voltage.

....

b)   Andy has built a radio which needs a 20 V electricity supply. The mains supply to Andy's house is 230 V. How could Andy adapt the transformer described above to make it suitable for his radio?

....

....

....

....

Top Tips: **Isolating** transformers seem a bit pointless on the face of it, but they're actually rather useful in a few **specific circumstances**. No, I'm not going to tell you which, it'd spoil Q10.

Diodes and Rectification

Q1 Match up each keyword with the correct description.

Semiconductor

n-type semiconductor

p-type semiconductor

Diode

has empty spaces called "holes" where electrons are missing

conducts electricity but not as well as a conductor

allows a current to flow in one direction only

has extra free electrons

Q2 a) Tick the boxes to show whether the following statements are **true** or **false**.

True False

i) The element silicon is a semiconductor.

ii) Semiconductors have low resistance in one direction and high resistance in the other.

iii) n-type semiconductors contain impurities but p-type semiconductors do not.

iv) 'Holes' effectively have a positive charge.

v) You need both p- and n-type semiconductors in a diode.

b) Write down correct versions of the false statements.

....

....

....

....

....

Q3 Diodes can be used to **rectify** AC current.

a) i) What does 'rectification' mean?

....

ii) Why is it sometimes necessary to rectify an AC current?

....

b) Which is the simpler method — half-wave rectification or full-wave rectification?

....

c) How many diodes are required for full-wave rectification?

....

<u>*Diodes and Rectification*</u>

Q4   Why are impurities are deliberately put into semiconductors?

....

Q5   Describe what happens to the 'holes' and electrons at the p-n junction
in a diode when there is **no potential difference** across the diode.

....

....

Q6   Explain, in terms of the movement of electrons, why a current flows in circuit A but not in circuit B.

Circuit A   **Circuit B**

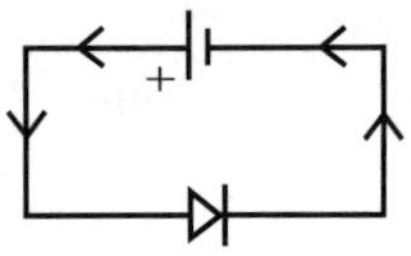

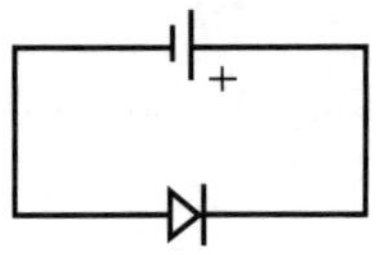

For this one, a sketched diagram on a bit of scrap paper might
help. Or you could think about where the electrons "want" to go.

....

....

....

....

Q7   A single diode in series with an AC supply gives **half-wave rectification**.

a)   Complete the diagram below to show the output voltage over time from the circuit shown.

<u>HALF-WAVE RECTIFICATION</u>

Output
voltage

Input Voltage   Output voltage

Time   Time

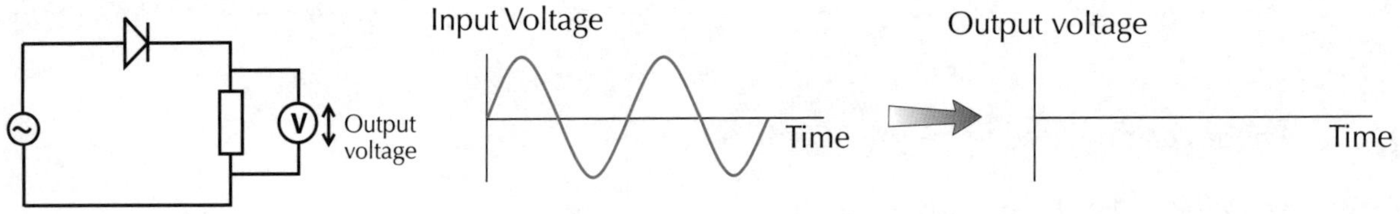

b)   The diagram shows a bridge circuit which
could be used to give **full-wave rectification**,
but the diodes are missing.

Complete the diagram to show
the position of the diodes in circuit.

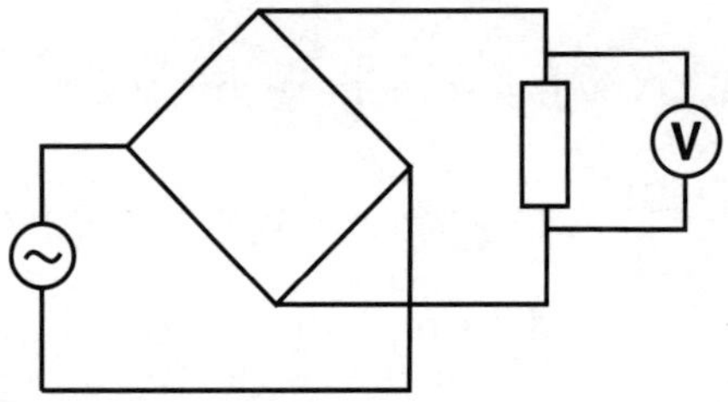

Top Tips: Yes, the circuit for Q7 b) is a bit of a pig. It's something that could come up in
the exam, though, so **be prepared** to sketch it out. If you can explain how it works, so much the
better. It's well worth learning how p-type and n-type semiconductors make a diode work, too.

Capacitors

Q1   Describe how to **fully charge** a capacitor.

....

....

Q2 a) Indicate whether the following statements are **true** or **false**.   True   False

   i) The higher the voltage of the power supply, the more charge a capacitor can store.   ☐   ☐

   ii) A capacitor can be used to store electric current.   ☐   ☐

   b) Write correct versions of any false statements.

....

....

Q3   Capacitors are used in **smoothing circuits** like the one shown.

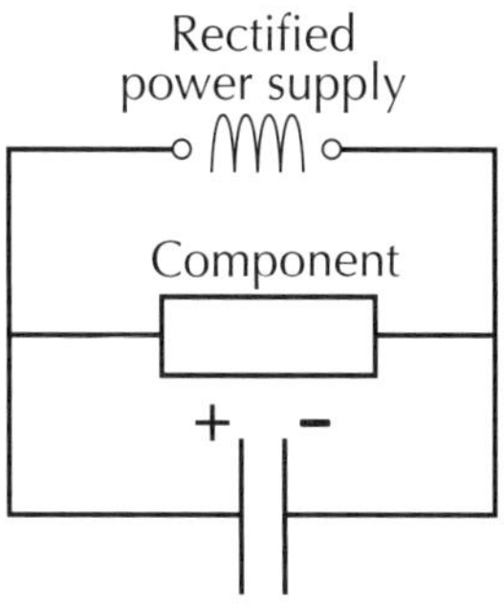

   a) Why is it often necessary to smooth a rectified AC voltage?

....

....

   b) Where does current flow when the input voltage is **high**?

....

   c) Where does current flow when the input voltage is **low**?

....

   d) Explain why the current through the component stays more or less steady.

....

....

Q4   The diagram shows a **time delay** circuit. When the power supply to the
circuit is switched on it takes a while for the output voltage, V_{out}, to rise.

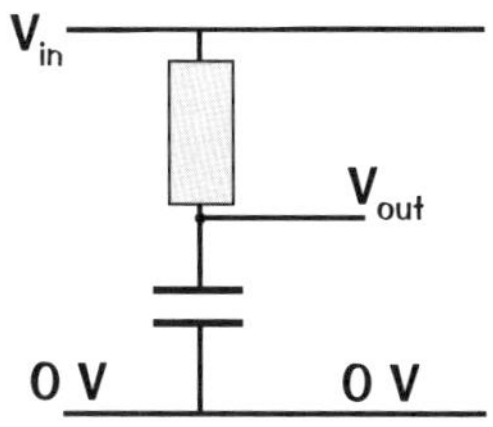

The sentences below explain how the time delay circuit works.
Complete them by circling the correct words or phrases.

   1. Initially the capacitor is fully charged / has no charge stored, so the
voltage across it is large / small and the output voltage is large / small.

   2. Charge flows into the capacitor so the voltage across it gradually increases / decreases and
the voltage across the resistor increases / decreases.

   3. As this happens the output voltage gradually rises / falls.

Logic Gates

Q1 Fill in the gaps in the following sentences about logic gates.

a) An electronic system in which the only possible values are **on** and **off**

is described as a .... system.

b) A **NOT** gate is sometimes called an ....

c) The five main kinds of logic gate are ....

Q2 Write the **correct component name** under each symbol.

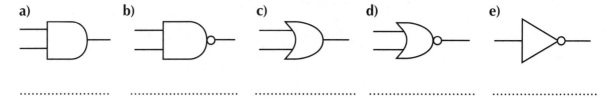

a)   b)   c)   d)   e)

....

Q3 What kind of logic gate would give each of the truth tables below?
Write the correct title and draw the correct symbol under each truth table.

A	B	Output
0	0	1
0	1	0
1	0	0
1	1	0

A	B	Output
0	0	0
0	1	0
1	0	0
1	1	1

A	B	Output
0	0	0
0	1	1
1	0	1
1	1	0

in	out
0	1
1	0

....

Q4 Peter draws a truth table for a **NAND** gate. He makes mistakes.

a) Correct his mistakes in the table.

b) What combination of two gates
would be the same as a NAND gate?

.... then ....

A	B	Output
0	0	0
0	1	1
1	0	1
1	1	1

Q5 For each of the following descriptions, write down the **name** of the **logic gate** which fits.

a) Output is 0 unless all inputs are 0. ....

b) Output is 1 if input is 0. ....

c) The only time output is 1 is when both inputs are 1. ....

d) Output is 1 unless both inputs are 1. ....

Using Logic Gates

Q1   This diagram shows a **logic circuit**.

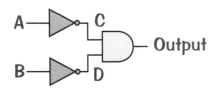

A	B	C	D	Output
0	0			
1	0			
0	1			
1	1			

Marie thinks that this logic circuit might be the same as a **NOR** gate. She plans a truth table to prove it:

a)   Finish the truth table by inserting all the missing values.

b)   Was Marie's idea correct — is this circuit the same as a NOR gate? ....

Q2   Mr Green's shop has **three doors**.
He wants a bell to ring if **any** door opens.

He designs the following logic circuit.

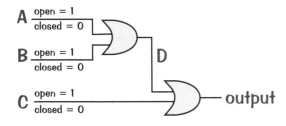

A	B	C	D	Output
0	0	0		
0	0	1		
0	1	0		
0	1	1		
1	0	0		
1	0	1		
1	1	0		
1	1	1		

a)   Complete the truth table for the logic circuit.

b)   Will the bell ring when **any one** door is opened? ....

c)   Will the bell ring if **two or more** doors are opened? ....

Q3   This diagram shows a **NOR** latch circuit
connected to a warning light.

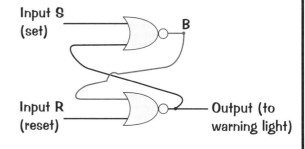

a)   Initially, both inputs are 0 and the light is off.

   i)   **Input S** changes to **1**. Explain what happens.

   ....

   ....

   ....

   ii)   Input S changes back to **0** again. What happens now? Explain your answer.

   ....

   ....

b)   If the main output is **1**, explain how it can be **reset** (to 0). ....

....

LEDs and Relays in Logic Circuits

Q1   Indicate whether the following statements are **true** or **false**.

		True	False
a)	Current can only flow one way through an LED.	☐	☐
b)	LEDs need a large current to work.	☐	☐
c)	An LED uses very little power.	☐	☐

Q2   LEDs can be used to show the output of a **logic gate**.

a)   Write down **two** reasons why LEDs rather than ordinary lamp bulbs are used in logic circuits.

....

....

b)   Why is an LED usually connected in series with a resistor?

....

Q3   Logic gates are often used to switch devices on and off.

a)   Explain why logic gates can't be used to switch devices on and off in **high current** circuits.

....

b)   Suggest how a logic circuit could be used to switch on a starter motor, even though the starter motor needs a high current.

....

....

Q4   A relay uses an **electromagnet** to connect two circuits.

a)   Explain how the logic circuit shown in the diagram can switch the high-current circuit on and off.

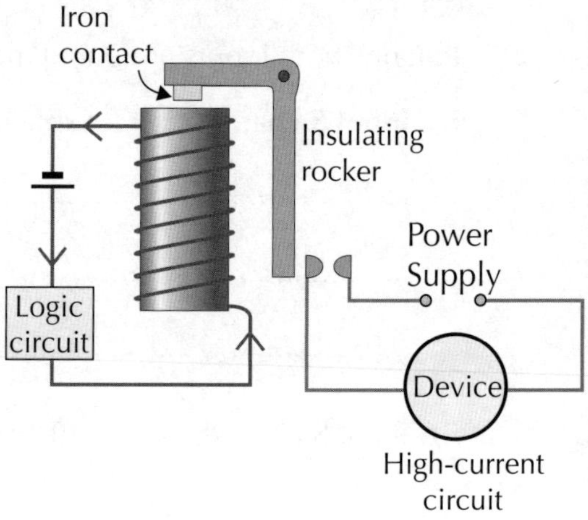

....

....

....

....

....

b)   Describe a safety benefit of using a relay to switch on or off a device which requires a large current.

....

Mixed Questions — Module P6

Q1 Emma did an experiment to test the **resistance** of two wires, X and Y.

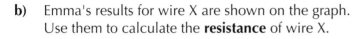

a) Emma used the standard test circuit shown to test the wires.
What is **component Z**? ....

b) Emma's results for wire X are shown on the graph.
Use them to calculate the **resistance** of wire X.

....

c) Wire Y has a resistance of **5 Ω**. Add the results you would
expect for this wire to the graph.

d) Emma then puts **both** wires in a circuit together.
Part of the circuit is as shown.
Calculate V₁ and V₂.

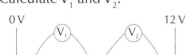

V_1 ....

V_2 ....

Q2 Bob wants a warning light to come on if a storeroom door is **closed** and the light inside is left **on**.

a) He realises that he needs to use **logic gates** in his system.
Sadly he gets it wrong and sets up the system shown.

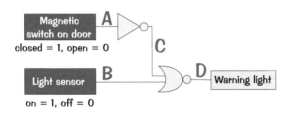

Inputs		C	D
A	B		

i) Fill in the truth table to show what happens in his system.

ii) In which circumstances will the light come on? ....

iii) Bob only actually needed to use **one** logic gate. Which was it? ....

b) Bob uses an **LDR** in the potential divider shown to sense
whether the store room light is on. Explain how this works.

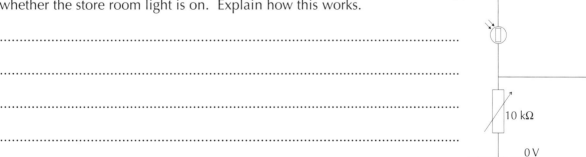

....

....

....

....

c) Bob decides he wants a **fan** to come on instead of the warning light.
He discovers he needs to use a relay. Apart from safety considerations, why is this?

....

Mixed Questions — Module P6

Q3 The diagram below shows a simple **motor**. The coil is rotating as shown.

a) Draw arrows labelled 'F' to show the direction of the **force** on each arm of the coil.

b) Draw arrows labelled 'I' on each arm of the coil to show the direction the **current** is flowing.

c) Draw '+' and '−' on the leads of the split-ring commutator to show the **polarity** of the power supply.

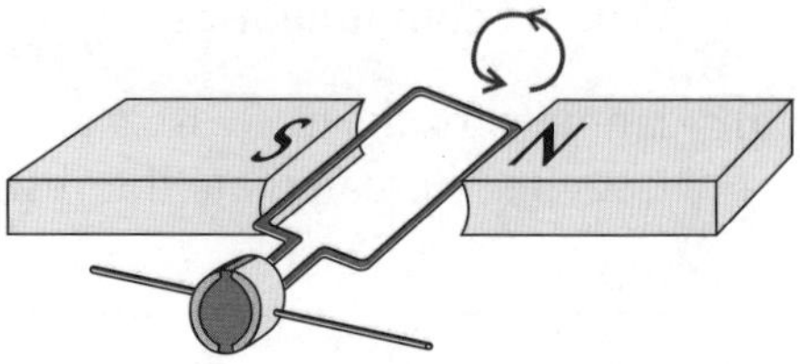

d) Explain the advantage of using a **rectangular** coil in a motor.

....

Q4 The diagram shows a **hamster-powered dynamo**.

a) What happens in the coil of wire when the hamster runs at a constant speed? Explain your answer.

....

....

....

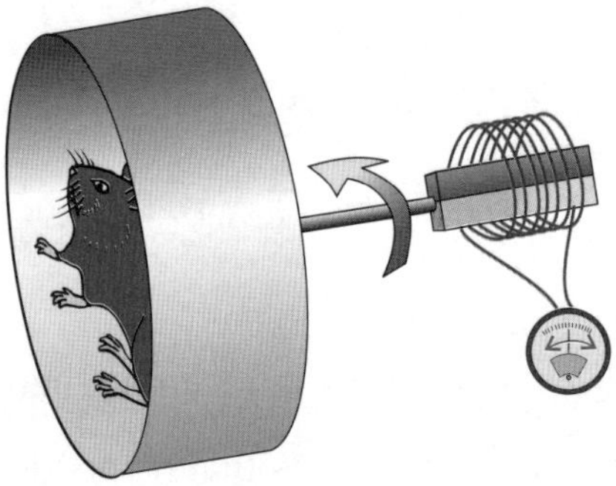

b) What would change if the hamster ran in the opposite direction (at the same speed as before)?

....

c) Meg wants to use the dynamo to charge her mobile phone, which requires a 12 V electrical supply. The dynamo supplies 2 V to the primary coil of a transformer which has 24 turns. How many turns must there be on the secondary coil?

....

Q5 A radio requires a **direct current**. A bridge circuit is used to **rectify** the AC current supply.

a) Which diodes would the current flow through when:

i) X is positive? ....

ii) X is negative? ....

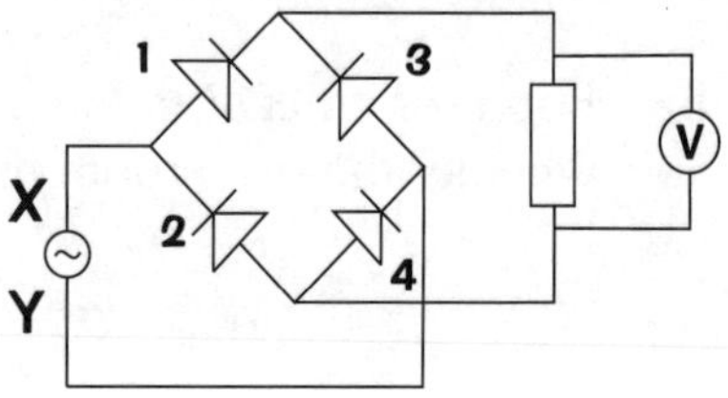

b) Sketch the output voltage you would expect from this circuit on the axes given.

c) Before this output/electricity supply can be used for the radio it must be **smoothed**.

i) Add the smoothed voltage to the diagram in part b).

ii) Name the component needed to smooth the voltage and draw its circuit symbol.

V_{out} ↑

→ **Time**

Component: .... **Symbol:** ....

PRW41